PRACTICAL WELLNESS COLLECTION

by

Ivette Smith

Contents

Ivette Smith

FIRST BOOK

THE LITTLE BOOK OF SELF-HELP

INTRODUCTION

There was an instance, amidst a cluttered shelf of brightly colored spines promising life-altering revelations, when I realized the self-help industry was both a beacon of hope and a bewildering maze. I stood there, a book in each hand, one advocating for relentless change, the other preaching the virtues of acceptance. It struck me that navigating this contradictory terrain was a challenge, yet here I was, still searching for something real amidst the promises.

Like many of you, my journey through the self-help landscape has been extensive and, at times, exasperating. I've turned the pages of countless books, each offering the secret formula to a fulfilled life. Yet, what became increasingly clear was that no amount of positive thinking could substitute for actual, deliberate action. This realization didn't come easy or quickly, but it has profoundly shaped my approach to personal growth.

This book is born from a desire to cut through the din of the self-help genre. It is grounded in scientific research and enriched by personal insights, offering a clear, practical guide to transforming your life. We will explore crucial themes like habit formation, the art of overcoming procrastination, and the power of consistency. We'll unlock creative thinking and learn to embrace change superficially but in ways that align deeply with who we are.

But this is not just any self-help book. Here, you are encouraged to engage actively, to sift through scientific insights and practical advice to find what truly resonates with your circumstances and goals. This book is interactive, with self-assessments and prompts inviting reflection and action.

When you turn the final page, you won't just be inspired. You will have a personalized, actionable plan that can lead to lasting changes in your life. If you are ready to commit to the journey, this could be the last self-help book you will ever need.

I invite you to approach this book with an open mind and a willing heart, ready to explore, learn, and grow. Consider it a read and a step towards profound personal discovery and growth.

Let's embark on this transformative journey together, with the promise that you have the strength and capability to reshape your life. I believe in you and your ability to navigate towards your desired future. Let this book be your guide, your companion, and perhaps, your final push toward the life you've always wanted.

THE PSYCHOLOGY BEHIND SELF-HELP

Every once in a while, you encounter a moment that subtly, yet profoundly, shifts your perspective; for me, it was one morning, drinking my coffee and looking out the window as the sun painted the sky with the promise of a new day; a simple truth dawned on me: our lives are essentially the sum of our habits. Whether tying our shoes, brushing our teeth, or scrolling through our phones, these small, repeated actions carve a path that shapes our existence. This realization sparked a fascination with the psychological underpinnings of self-help, specifically how understanding the mechanics of our mind can empower us to live better, more fulfilling lives.

This chapter delves into the fascinating world of psychology that supports self-help theories and practices. Here, we uncover the foundational principles that can make the difference between fleeting attempts at change and lasting transformation. Our exploration is about understanding what makes us tick and applying this knowledge in practical, meaningful ways.

Decoding Habit Formation: The Science of Making or Breaking a Habit

Understanding the Habit Loop

At the heart of every habit is a simple yet powerful process called the habit loop. This loop consists of three key elements: a cue, a routine, and a reward. The cue triggers your brain to initiate a behavior, the routine is the behavior itself, and the reward is the benefit you gain from it. Recognizing this cycle is the first step in mastering your habits. For instance, your morning alarm (cue) prompts you to brush your teeth (routine), and the feeling of freshness (reward) reinforces this action. By dissecting your habits into these components, you can untangle and reshape your daily practices to align with your aspirations.

Neuroplasticity and Habit Change

Neuroplasticity, or your brain's ability to reorganize itself by forming new neural connections throughout life, plays a crucial role in habit formation and change. Each time you perform a task, whether playing the piano or choosing a healthy snack, you strengthen the neural pathways associated with that behavior. Over time, these paths become more defined, making the behavior more automatic. The beauty of neuroplasticity lies in its two-way street; just as habits can be formed, they can be reshaped or extinguished. Understanding this gives you the power to break free from detrimental routines and forge new, positive ones.

The Power of Incremental Change

While grand gestures can be thrilling, small, incremental changes lead to sustainable transformations. Consider adding just one healthy food to your diet each week. Such a modest change might initially seem insignificant, but these small additions can lead to a wholly revitalized diet. This approach lowers the mental barriers to change, making it easier to stick with new behaviors until they solidify into habits. This principle, often summarized as "small steps lead to big changes," is rooted in the understanding that gradual adjustments are more manageable, less overwhelming, and more likely to become permanent habits. Here's an in-depth look at why incremental change is so powerful and how it can be effectively applied in various aspects of life:

Psychological Underpinnings

Lowering Mental Barriers Incremental changes lower the mental barriers to change. When faced with significant shifts, our minds can perceive them as threats, triggering resistance and fear. Breaking down these shifts into smaller, more manageable steps reduces the psychological strain and makes the process feel less daunting.

Building Confidence and Momentum

Each small change successfully implemented builds confidence and creates a sense of accomplishment. This positive reinforcement fuels motivation and makes subsequent changes feel more achievable. As these small successes accumulate, they create a momentum that propels further progress.

Practical Applications

Diet and Nutrition Consider the practice of adding just one healthy food to your diet each week. This modest change might initially seem insignificant, but clearly, recording these small additions can lead to a wholly revitalized diet over time. For example:

- **Week 1:** Incorporate an extra serving of vegetables each day.

- **Week 2:** Replace sugary drinks with water or herbal tea.

- **Week 3:** Add a handful of nuts or seeds as a daily snack.

These gradual changes help your palate adjust, making it easier to maintain these habits in the long run. Collectively, they can significantly improve your nutritional intake.

Exercise and Fitness The same principle applies to physical fitness. Instead of committing to an intensive workout regimen from the outset, start with small, manageable activities:

- **Week 1:** Take a 10-minute walk each day.

- **Week 2:** Add a few minutes of stretching or yoga.

- **Week 3:** Incorporate short strength-training exercises.

By gradually increasing the intensity and duration of your workouts, you can build a sustainable exercise routine that becomes a natural part of your daily life.

Personal Development and Skills Incremental change is also effective in personal development. For instance, if you aim to read more books:

- **Week 1:** Read ten pages each day.
- **Week 2:** Increase to 15 pages.
- **Week 3:** Dedicate 20 minutes each morning to reading.

This approach makes the goal less intimidating and helps you develop a consistent reading habit.

The Role of Consistency

Consistency is the key to making small steps lead to monumental changes. Regularly performing these small actions embeds them into your routine, transforming them into automatic behaviors. Over time, these consistent efforts compound, leading to significant, lasting transformation.

Habit Stacking

One effective strategy to maintain consistency is habit stacking, which involves linking new habits to existing ones. For example, if you want to start meditating, you could link it to your morning coffee routine:

- Make coffee (existing habit).
- While it brews, meditate for 5 minutes (new habit).

By associating the new habit with an established one, you create a cue that triggers the desired behavior, making it easier to adopt and maintain.

Long-Term Impact

Compounding Benefits Just as compound interest accumulates in finance, the benefits of small, incremental changes compound over time. Each positive action builds upon the previous one, creating a ripple effect that enhances multiple areas of your life.

Sustainable Lifestyle Changes Unlike drastic changes that can be difficult to sustain, incremental changes blend seamlessly into your lifestyle. They adapt to your pace and capacity, allowing you to progress continuously without feeling overwhelmed or discouraged.

Enhanced Resilience

Gradual change fosters resilience by teaching you to adapt and persevere through minor setbacks. When changes are small, it's easier to recover from slip-ups and stay committed to your goals.

Creating a Supportive Environment for Change

Your environment plays a pivotal role in shaping your habits. Everything from your kitchen layout to your office's design can influence your behavior. Creating an environment that makes these habits more likely to be maintained is essential to fostering positive habits. For example, if you're trying to cultivate a habit of reading before bed, keeping a book on your nightstand makes it more likely that you'll pick it up. Similarly, try charging your phone away from your bed to reduce screen time. By tweaking your surroundings to support your goals, you can nudge yourself towards better habits and away from those that derail your progress.

The Importance of Accountability and Support

Accountability and support from others can significantly enhance your habit-forming efforts. Sharing your goals with friends or family creates a sense of responsibility and encouragement. Joining groups or communities with similar objectives can provide additional motivation and practical tips. This social aspect of habit formation helps sustain your commitment and provides a network of encouragement when challenges arise.

Reflecting and Adapting

Regular reflection on your progress is crucial for habit formation. Evaluating what is working and what isn't allows you to adjust your strategies accordingly. This reflection helps you identify obstacles and find creative solutions to overcome them. Keeping a journal or using a habit-tracking app can facilitate this process by providing a clear record of your journey and highlighting patterns that might otherwise go unnoticed.

Embracing the Journey

Habit formation is a continuous journey rather than a destination. Embracing this perspective helps you stay patient and resilient, even when progress seems slow. Celebrating small victories along the way can boost your morale and reinforce your commitment. Remember that setbacks are part of the process and provide valuable learning opportunities. With persistence and a positive outlook, you can transform your habits and, ultimately, your life. Embracing the power of incremental change is about shifting your mindset from seeking instant gratification to valuing steady, consistent progress.

This exploration of habit formation enlightens and empowers you to take control of your actions and, by extension, your life. With these insights, you are better equipped to craft a daily routine that brings you closer to the person you aspire to be and enriches your life in ways that grand gestures alone could never achieve

The Truth About Motivation: Why It Fades and How to Keep It Alive

Motivation, that initial spark that propels us toward our goals, is a fascinating psychological phenomenon. It is often classified into two main types: intrinsic and extrinsic. Intrinsic motivation comes from within; it is driven by an interest or enjoyment in the task, such as a hobby you pursue because it makes you happy. On the other hand, extrinsic motivation involves performing a behavior to earn a reward or avoid punishment, like working extra hours to receive a bonus. Understanding these motivations is crucial as they influence the strength and sustainability of our drive to act.

The Nature of Intrinsic and Extrinsic Motivation

The robustness of intrinsic motivation, where the activity is the reward, often leads to deeper and more persistent engagement. This type of motivation encourages us to explore, learn, and persist through challenges because the process brings satisfaction. Intrinsic motivation is closely linked to personal growth and fulfillment, as it aligns with our interests, passions, and values. When intrinsically motivated, we are more likely to experience a state of flow where we are fully absorbed and find joy in the activity itself.

Extrinsic motivation, while effective in the short term, often depends on external factors that may not always be consistent or within our control, making this type more susceptible to diminishing over time. Extrinsic motivators, such as rewards, recognition, or avoidance of negative consequences, can initiate action and provide direction but may not sustain long-term engagement. Over-reliance on extrinsic motivation can lead to a dependency on external validation and diminish our intrinsic drive.

The Fading of Motivation

This fading of motivation, mainly extrinsic, is a phenomenon well-documented in psychological studies. Initially, when a new goal is set, motivation spikes. The novelty and excitement of pursuing something new can provide a powerful boost. However, as time progresses and challenges or routines set in, the intensity of motivation can wane. This decline is often due to several factors, including habituation to the activity, decreased novelty, and the sometimes slow pace of progress, which aligns differently from the fast reward feedback that initially boosted our motivation. Moreover, the "hedonic treadmill" effect illustrates how our expectations and satisfaction levels adjust over time, making the same rewards less satisfying. This understanding is crucial for anyone seeking lasting change, as it underscores the limitation of relying solely on motivation to achieve long-term goals. Recognizing the transient nature of motivation prompts us to seek more stable sources of drive and commitment.

Building Discipline and Willpower

Building discipline and cultivating willpower are essential for maintaining momentum when motivation declines. Discipline, often misunderstood merely as a rigid structure, is about creating a framework within which we operate. It's about setting up systems that support consistency—turning beneficial actions into non-negotiable parts of our day. This could look like setting a specific time for exercise each day, which, over time, transforms from a conscious effort into a regular part of your routine.

Similarly, by regularly challenging oneself to small tasks that require self-control, willpower can be strengthened, gradually increasing in difficulty. Willpower is like a muscle that can be trained; the more we use it, the stronger it becomes. However, just like muscles, it can also become fatigued, so managing our energy and setting realistic expectations is essential. Practicing self-discipline involves creating habits and routines that align with our long-term goals and values, reducing reliance on fleeting motivation.

The Power of Systems Over Goals

Setting up systems over merely setting goals can fundamentally shift how effectively individuals maintain their path toward personal achievement. Goals are essential for direction, but they remain aspirational without a system to carry out the necessary actions. Systems, however, are the daily activities and habits that inch us closer to our desired outcome. For instance, if your goal is to write a book, setting a system where you write a page a day transforms your approach. It shifts focus from the overwhelming concept of completing an entire book to a more manageable daily action. This system makes the task more achievable and ensures consistent progress, regardless of fluctuating motivation levels.

We emphasize systems to create a structure that supports continuous effort and progress. Systems help us break down larger goals into smaller, actionable steps, making the process less daunting and more sustainable. This approach fosters a sense of accomplishment and builds momentum, which can further enhance our intrinsic motivation.

Creating a Supportive Environment

Another critical factor in sustaining motivation is creating an environment that supports our goals. Our surroundings can significantly influence our behavior and decision-making processes. By designing an environment that minimizes distractions and promotes positive habits, we can make it easier to stay on track. This might involve organizing our workspace to reduce clutter, setting up reminders for important tasks, or surrounding ourselves with supportive and like-minded individuals who encourage our efforts.

Moreover, leveraging technology and tools, such as habit-tracking apps or productivity planners, can help reinforce our commitment and visually represent our progress. These tools can serve as external cues that trigger our routines and remind us of our goals, enhancing our intrinsic and extrinsic motivation.

The Importance of Reflection and Adaptation

Regular reflection on our progress is crucial for sustaining motivation and making necessary adjustments. Evaluating what is working and what isn't allows us to adapt our strategies and refine our systems. Reflection helps us identify potential obstacles and develop creative solutions to overcome them. Keeping a journal or using a habit-tracking app can facilitate this process by clearly recording our journey and highlighting patterns that might otherwise go unnoticed.

Adapting our approach based on reflection ensures that we remain flexible and responsive to changes in our circumstances and goals. It also fosters a growth mindset, where we view challenges as opportunities for learning and improvement. This mindset enhances our resilience and persistence, enabling us to stay motivated and committed long-term.

Motivation and habit formation are not destinations; they are constant explorations. Embracing this perspective helps us stay patient and resilient, even when progress seems slow. Celebrating small victories along the way can boost our morale and reinforce our commitment. Remember that stumbling blocks are part of the process and provide valuable learning opportunities. With persistence and a positive outlook, you can transform your habits and, ultimately, your life.

By integrating these insights into the fabric of our daily lives, we can build a more robust framework for achieving lasting change. Understanding the psychological underpinnings of motivation, combined with the development of discipline, the implementation of effective systems, and the creation of supportive environments, equips us with the tools to maintain our drive and achieve our goals. As we move forward, remember that the structure we build around our actions determines their longevity and impact.

Overcoming Procrastination: The Psychology Behind Delaying and How to Combat It

Procrastination, a familiar foe for many, often emerges not from a lack of desire to act but from deep-rooted psychological barriers. Among these, the fear of failure looms large, casting a shadow over our capacity to commence or continue tasks. This fear, paradoxically, can lead us to put off tasks to avoid the risk of failure, despite knowing that delay might increase the likelihood of the outcome we fear. Similarly, perfectionism plays a significant role. For perfectionists, the idea that a task must be completed flawlessly can create an overwhelming pressure that makes starting the task daunting. Decision paralysis also contributes to procrastination, particularly when faced with multiple choices or overwhelming options, leading to a sort of decision fatigue that makes it easier to avoid making any decision.

Understanding the Root Causes

Understanding these root causes is crucial because it allows us to address procrastination as a time management issue and a complex psychological challenge. Fear of failure can be deeply ingrained, often stemming from early experiences or societal pressures that associate self-worth with success. Perfectionism, on the other hand, is frequently linked to unrealistic standards and a fear of judgment. Decision paralysis is exacerbated by the modern world's many choices, creating a cognitive overload that impedes decision-making processes.

Tackling Procrastination with a Multifaceted Approach

Tackling procrastination requires a multifaceted approach, beginning with acknowledging these underlying fears and pressures. Recognizing procrastination as often a protective response to less obvious anxieties can be liberating. It shifts the focus from self-blame to a more compassionate, understanding approach towards self-management. This shift is vital in creating an environment where one can employ practical strategies without the additional burden of self-criticism, which can be a significant barrier to progress.

Mindfulness as a Tool for Combatting Procrastination

Mindfulness has emerged as a powerful tool in combating procrastination. By fostering an increased awareness of the present moment, mindfulness techniques reduce the anxiety associated with future tasks that often lead to procrastination. For example, when a task feels overwhelming, taking a moment to engage in a brief mindfulness exercise, such as focused breathing or a body scan, can help reset your mental state and reduce the looming anxiety that may be causing the delay. This practice helps center the mind, making it easier to approach tasks with a calmer, more focused attitude.

Creating Systems of Accountability

Creating systems of accountability is another cornerstone in the fight against procrastination. Whether through peer support—partnering with a colleague or friend to check in on each other's progress—or through public commitment, such as declaring goals on social media or a blog, accountability can significantly enhance commitment to task completion. Knowing that others are aware of your goals and are perhaps tracking your progress can be a powerful motivator. It adds a layer of external encouragement and, occasionally, pressure, which can be beneficial when internal motivation wavers.

Practical Strategies to Overcome Procrastination

These strategies offer a practical approach to understanding and overcoming the psychological barriers that foster procrastination. By addressing the root causes and implementing targeted techniques, we can see a shift in managing our time and approaching our tasks. Here are some additional strategies to combat procrastination:

<u>Breaking Tasks into Smaller Steps</u>: Large tasks can be intimidating, leading to avoidance. Breaking tasks into smaller, manageable steps makes them less daunting and easier to start. Each small accomplishment builds momentum, making it easier to continue.

<u>Setting Realistic Goals</u>: Setting achievable goals helps maintain motivation. Unrealistic goals can lead to frustration and increased procrastination. Setting realistic, attainable goals creates a sense of progress and accomplishment.

<u>Utilizing the Pomodoro Technique</u>: This time management method involves working for a set period (usually 25 minutes) followed by a short break. This technique can improve focus and productivity, making it easier to tackle tasks without feeling overwhelmed. (We will learn more about this technique in a later chapter).

<u>Eliminating Distractions</u>: Creating a workspace free from distractions can enhance concentration. This might involve turning off notifications, setting boundaries with others, or using apps that block distracting websites.

<u>Rewarding Progress:</u> Positive reinforcement can be a powerful motivator. Rewarding yourself for completing tasks, no matter how small, can encourage continued effort and reduce procrastination.

Addressing Procrastination with Cognitive Behavioral Techniques

Cognitive Behavioral Therapy (CBT) techniques can also effectively address procrastination. CBT focuses on identifying and challenging negative thought patterns that contribute to procrastination. By restructuring these thoughts, you can change the associated behaviors. For example, replacing thoughts like "I'll never be able to finish this" with "I can start with one small step" can reduce the anxiety and fear that fuel procrastination.

Building Resilience and Adaptability

Building resilience and adaptability is crucial in overcoming procrastination. Life is unpredictable, and setbacks are inevitable. Developing the ability to adapt to changing circumstances and bounce back from failures can reduce the tendency to procrastinate in response to challenges. This involves cultivating a growth mindset, where you view challenges as opportunities for learning and improvement rather than threats to your self-worth.

Procrastination is not a defining trait but a challenge that needs to be navigated and overcome with the right tools and mindset. By understanding the psychological underpinnings of procrastination, such as fear of failure, perfectionism, and decision paralysis, we can develop strategies to address these barriers. Incorporating mindfulness, accountability, practical time management techniques, and cognitive behavioral approaches can help combat procrastination. Embracing a compassionate and proactive approach towards self-management and building resilience and adaptability equips us to overcome procrastination and achieve our goals.

The Role of Mindset in Personal Transformation: Fixed vs. Growth Perspectives

The concept of mindset, as explored by psychologist Carol Dweck, has significantly shifted our understanding of how our thoughts and beliefs about our abilities influence our behavior and predict our success. Dweck categorizes mindset into two distinct types: fixed and growth. A fixed mindset assumes that our character, intelligence, and creative abilities are static givens that we can't change in any meaningful way, and success is the affirmation of that inherent intelligence, an assessment of how those givens measure up against an equally fixed standard. Conversely, a growth mindset thrives on challenge and sees failure not as evidence of unintelligence but as a heartening springboard for growth and stretching our existing abilities.

The limitations imposed by a fixed mindset are profound. It creates an urgency to prove oneself repeatedly, interpreting every encounter as a test of one's worthiness. In this mindset, every failure is a crushing defeat, a painful declaration of unfitness. Therefore, the fear of facing challenges becomes paralyzing because failure means a negative judgment of one's basic capabilities. People with a fixed mindset avoid tasks where they might fail, thereby forfeiting opportunities for learning and growth. This avoidance, in turn, solidifies the very boundaries they fear to test, creating a cycle of stagnation that can be difficult to break.

Cultivating a growth mindset, on the other hand, involves recognizing that the brain, like muscles, becomes stronger with use. Challenges, therefore, are opportunities to strengthen one's mental faculties. Strategies to nurture a growth mindset, in a nutshell, include:

1. Embracing challenges.

2. Persisting in the face of setbacks.

3. Valuing effort over inherent talent.

Accepting challenges can be as simple as choosing a new skill to learn, regardless of the initial difficulty. Persistence can be cultivated by setting long-term goals where setbacks are likely and committing to progress despite the obstacles. Valuing effort means recognizing that effort is a path to mastery and celebrating minor improvements as signs of progress, not endpoints.

In applying a growth mindset to self-help, the transformation is evident in how challenges are approached. A growth mindset encourages resilience and adaptability—qualities essential for personal development. It shifts the focus from proving oneself to improving oneself. This perspective enhances the effectiveness of self-help strategies and ensures they are approached with the right attitude—an openness to learn and a readiness to adapt. For instance, if a recommended strategy does not work as expected, instead of viewing it as a failure, a growth mindset would analyze what can be learned from the experience and how the approach can be adjusted for better results. This iterative process is fundamental in self-help, where personal growth is often a matter of trial and adjustment.

Moreover, a growth mindset instills a love of learning, which is critical in the self-help journey. It transforms the quest for personal improvement from a chore or a series of hurdles into an exciting exploration of one's potential. This love for learning fuels sustained engagement with self-help techniques, even when progress seems slow or invisible, because the focus is on the growth journey, not merely on reaching a destination. This perspective is crucial because personal transformation is rarely linear and often requires sustained effort and continual learning.

The implications of adopting a growth mindset extend beyond personal success. They determine how one deals with feedback, overcomes challenges, and interacts with others. It is of such value that I dedicate a whole chapter to it. In a constantly changing world, adapting and growing is invaluable; a growth mindset provides the framework for this adaptability. By viewing abilities as qualities that can be developed, a growth mindset fosters a resilience that is essential not just for personal development but for navigating the complexities of modern life. It encourages an active engagement with life's challenges, transforming potential obstacles into opportunities for personal and professional growth.

Understanding Your Brain on Stress: Strategies for Management and Relief

Stress, an inevitable part of life, affects us all. You might notice it as a tightness in your shoulders during a busy workday or feel its grip as anxiety before an important event. Understanding stress and its physiological basis is crucial in managing it effectively. When faced with a stressor, your body responds with a series of biological changes: your heart rate increases, your breath quickens, and your muscles tense, ready for action. This response, known as the fight-or-flight response, involves the release of hormones such as adrenaline and cortisol. While this response is vital for survival, enabling humans to respond quickly to threats, its activation during non-life-threatening situations can lead to complications.

The effects of this response are not limited to one's immediate health but can extend to long-term physical and mental well-being. Chronic stress, which occurs when this response is triggered repeatedly or when stressors persist over a long time, can lead to a myriad of health issues. It can disrupt nearly every system in your body. It can suppress your immune system, upset your digestive and reproductive systems, increase the risk of heart attack and stroke, and speed up the aging process. On the mental health front, chronic stress is a key contributor to anxiety and depression, making it crucial to manage stress effectively.

Mindfulness and relaxation techniques stand out as beacons of relief in managing stress. Mindfulness, the practice of maintaining a nonjudgmental state of heightened or complete awareness of one's thoughts, emotions, or experiences on a moment-to-moment basis, can significantly mitigate the effects of stress. Deep breathing, meditation, and progressive muscle relaxation are particularly effective. For example, deep breathing helps counter stress's effects by slowing the heart rate and lowering blood pressure, creating a feeling of calm. Meditation, on the other hand, can help build skills to manage stress, increase self-awareness, and offer a break from stressors, reducing the impact on your body. Progressive muscle relaxation, which involves tightening and relaxing different muscle groups, can relieve physical tension and psychological stress.

Implementing lifestyle changes can also play a significant role in reducing stress. Regular physical exercise is not only good for your physical health but also helps to relieve stress. Exercise produces endorphins (chemicals in the brain that act as natural painkillers) and improves the ability to sleep, reducing stress and anxiety. Studies suggest aerobic exercise can decrease overall tension levels, elevate and stabilize mood, improve sleep, and improve self-esteem. Even five minutes of aerobic exercise can stimulate anti-anxiety effects. Another significant aspect of lifestyle modification is sleep hygiene. Improving sleep can reduce stress by strengthening the mind's resilience to stress. Establishing a regular, relaxing bedtime routine, such as taking a warm bath or reading a book, can promote better sleep.

Additionally, social support is vital in managing stress. Being part of a friend network gives your life an added support layer. Good relationships with friends and loved ones are essential to any healthy lifestyle and vital when you're stressed. A reassuring voice, even for a minute, can put everything in perspective. Creating systems of accountability is another cornerstone in the fight against procrastination. Whether through peer support—partnering with a colleague or friend to check in on each other's progress—or through public commitment, such as declaring goals on social media or a blog, accountability can significantly enhance commitment to task completion. Knowing that others are aware of your goals and are perhaps tracking your progress can be a powerful motivator. It adds a layer of external encouragement and, occasionally, pressure, which can be beneficial when internal motivation wavers.

Stress, often viewed as an inescapable part of life, can be managed by understanding its roots and applying practical strategies to reduce its impact. By recognizing the signs of stress and responding with effective management techniques, from mindfulness to lifestyle adjustments, you empower yourself to lead a healthier, more balanced life. These tools help manage stress and enhance your overall well-being, enabling you to meet challenges with resilience and poise. As we navigate life's pressures, let us remember that the power to manage stress lies within us through our actions and mindset.

Evaluating Popular Self-Help Myths

In a world that often celebrates the spectacle of success, it's easy to fall for the allure of overnight transformations. The stories are everywhere, splashed across glossy magazine covers and dominating our social media feeds, telling tales of individuals who seemingly achieved vast success with little effort. But as you peel back the layers of these captivating narratives, the truth often reveals a very different story—one of relentless perseverance, numerous setbacks, and the kind of resilience that turns ordinary individuals into exemplars of success. This chapter aims to dismantle some of the most pervasive myths in self-help, guiding you toward a more informed and realistic path to personal achievement.

The Reality of Success

The Myth of Overnight Success: Setting Realistic Expectations

The belief in overnight success is one of the most enduring myths in our culture. It's a compelling narrative: someone picks up a guitar and becomes a rock star in just a few short months. Or, an author writes a book in a frenzy of inspiration, and it becomes an instant bestseller. However, what often goes unseen behind these sensationalized stories are the years of practice, the late nights, the rejected drafts, and the unwavering commitment to a vision. True success is not a momentary flash of achievement but a slow, ongoing process of growth and perseverance. It requires resilience—the ability to recover from setbacks and keep moving forward, even when progress seems invisible.

Success, in its truest form, is the cumulative result of consistent effort and dedication over an extended period. The glamorous tales of instant fame are often exceptions rather than the norm, and they overlook the importance of the journey that leads to those moments of recognition. By understanding and embracing the reality that success is built over time, individuals can set more realistic expectations and develop a more sustainable approach to achieving their goals.

Success Stories Deconstructed

Consider J.K. Rowling, often cited as a "sudden" literary sensation. Before "Harry Potter" catapulted her to fame, Rowling faced numerous rejections from publishers. The world didn't see the moments of doubt, the persistence in refining her manuscripts, and her dedication to her craft despite discouraging feedback. Similarly, the tech giant Apple, revered for its innovation, resulted from years of experimentation and failures. Steve Jobs, now synonymous with success, experienced significant setbacks, including being ousted from the company he helped create before his eventual return and subsequent achievements. These stories underscore a crucial point: each setback was actually a stepping stone, an integral part of a more significant journey toward success. The path to success is often winding and filled with obstacles, but each challenge provides valuable lessons and opportunities for growth. By examining the detailed backstories of successful individuals and companies, we can gain a more comprehensive understanding of what it truly takes to achieve greatness.

Setting Realistic Goals and Expectations

To navigate your path to success, setting realistic goals is essential. This means understanding the difference between aspirational targets and achievable objectives. Realistic goals are clear, time-bound, and within your control. They account for learning curves and are adaptable to feedback and change. For example, rather than aiming to "become a successful entrepreneur," a more tangible goal would be to "launch a product prototype by the end of the year and seek feedback." This approach provides a clear direction and breaks down the larger goal into manageable steps, making the process less daunting and more actionable.

Setting realistic goals involves recognizing the effort and time required to achieve them. It also means being flexible and willing to adjust your plans as you encounter new information and experiences. By breaking down ambitious aspirations into smaller, more attainable milestones, you can maintain motivation and make steady progress toward your ultimate objectives.

The Power of Incremental Progress

One of the most effective ways to maintain motivation and perspective is to recognize and celebrate incremental progress—the small, daily victories contributing to a larger goal. This could be as simple as writing a single page of your novel daily or improving your running time by a few seconds. Each small success is a building block toward more significant achievement, and acknowledging these mini-milestones keeps your spirits up and your goals in sight. Moreover, this method helps to demystify the achievement of big goals by highlighting that they are the sum of consistent, small efforts.

Incremental progress emphasizes the importance of consistency and perseverance. By focusing on daily efforts and celebrating minor achievements, you build momentum and develop a habit of continuous improvement. This approach not only makes the journey toward your goals more manageable but also more rewarding, as you can regularly see and appreciate your progress.

Cultivating a Growth Mindset

A growth mindset (I will cover this in more detail in Chapter 4), the belief that abilities and intelligence can be developed through dedication and hard work, is crucial for setting realistic expectations and achieving success. Embracing a growth mindset allows you to view challenges as opportunities for learning and improvement rather than insurmountable obstacles. This perspective encourages resilience, adaptability, and a willingness to take risks, all of which are essential for long-term success.

Cultivating a growth mindset involves reframing your approach to failure and setbacks. Instead of seeing them as indicators of your limitations, view them as valuable feedback and opportunities to grow. By maintaining a positive and proactive attitude, you can overcome obstacles and continue making progress toward your goals.

Embracing the Journey

Exploring the myth of overnight success reveals that the real magic lies not in the rarity of sudden fame or fortune but in ordinary, persistent efforts toward a goal. Understanding this can transform your approach to personal and professional aspirations, grounding your journey in reality and preparing you for the hard work and inevitable setbacks that come with genuine, lasting success.

Success is not a destination but a journey. Embracing this journey with patience, perseverance, and a realistic understanding of what it entails allows you to enjoy the process and appreciate the growth and learning that occur along the way. By setting realistic goals, celebrating incremental progress, and maintaining a growth mindset, you can navigate the path to success with resilience and determination, ultimately achieving your aspirations in a sustainable and fulfilling manner.

Why "Just Think Positive" Isn't Always the Answer: A Balanced Approach to Optimism

The "just think positive" mantra has echoed through countless self-help books, seminars, and life coaching sessions. It's easy to see the appeal—after all, who wouldn't want to believe that positive thinking alone can pave the way to success and happiness? However, this approach can sometimes oversimplify the complex nature of human emotions and experiences. Relying solely on positive thinking risks ignoring deeper, underlying issues that require attention and can foster unrealistic expectations about what positivity can achieve. This is not to diminish the value of a positive outlook but rather to suggest that optimism is most effective when balanced with a healthy dose of realism.

Positive thinking, when unchecked, might lead you to overlook critical aspects of reality that need addressing. For example, you constantly tell yourself everything is fine when facing significant challenges at work or in personal relationships. In that case, you might miss opportunities to make necessary changes or seek help. Moreover, the pressure to maintain an optimistic facade can be exhausting and isolating, especially when you're not allowing yourself to feel and express a full range of emotions. This suppression can lead to increased stress and, paradoxically, to feelings of guilt or inadequacy for not always being happy.

Balanced Optimism

Balanced optimism represents a more sustainable approach. It involves acknowledging and accepting the reality of a situation while maintaining a hopeful outlook about the future. This balance allows you to prepare for various outcomes, including those that are less than ideal, which is crucial for managing potential setbacks effectively. For instance, if you're starting a new business, balanced optimism would lead you to maintain a positive outlook on your venture's success while also preparing for the possibility of initial failures or setbacks through contingency planning. This preparation might include setting aside a financial buffer or having a plan B for revenue during the early stages.

Balanced optimism also encourages a realistic assessment of your current situation, which can lead to more effective problem-solving. When you can look at challenges without the rose-colored glasses of unchecked positivity, you're more likely to identify actionable steps to overcome these challenges. For example, if you're struggling with a skill at your job, acknowledging this difficulty can lead you to seek additional training or mentorship rather than simply hoping the problem will resolve itself with a positive attitude.

Cognitive Behavioral Techniques

Cognitive Behavioral Therapy (CBT) offers valuable tools for cultivating a balanced outlook. CBT techniques help identify and challenge overly negative thought patterns and replace them with more realistic and balanced ones. For instance, if you tend to think, "I'll never be good at this," CBT would encourage you to examine the evidence for and against this thought, potentially leading you to a more balanced perspective like, "I'm not good at this yet, but I can improve with practice and effort." This technique, known as cognitive restructuring, can significantly alter your emotional responses and behaviors, leading to more positive outcomes in your personal and professional life.

Another useful CBT technique is the practice of mindfulness, which involves staying present and fully engaged with the current moment without judgment. Mindfulness can help you become more aware of your thoughts and feelings and gain distance from them, reducing the likelihood of being swept away by negative emotions. This practice can enhance your ability to remain poised in the face of life's challenges, fostering a balanced optimism by allowing you to acknowledge your current emotions without letting them dictate your actions.

Dialectical Behavior Therapy (DBT), on the other hand, emphasizes navigating emotional storms by teaching you to balance acceptance and change. It integrates mindfulness (being fully present at. the moment), distress tolerance (getting through tough times without making them worse), emotional regulation (managing and responding to intense feelings effectively), and interpersonal effectiveness to help individuals manage intense emotions and improve relationships.

Embracing a Full Spectrum of Emotions

A genuinely balanced perspective acknowledges that life encompasses many emotions, each serving a purpose. Emotions like sadness, frustration, and anger, often viewed negatively, can signal that something in your life needs attention. For example, feeling frustrated at work can be a catalyst for necessary changes or discussions that lead to a more fulfilling career path. Allowing yourself to experience and express these emotions can lead to deeper self-understanding and, ultimately, more meaningful changes in your life.

Moreover, accepting and expressing various emotions is crucial for building resilience and psychological flexibility. It's not about never feeling bad but how you respond to and recover from these emotions. Understanding and managing your emotional experiences allows you to navigate life's ups and downs more effectively, leading to greater well-being and satisfaction.

In conclusion, while positive thinking has its place, it is most effective when balanced with realism and a healthy acceptance of all emotional experiences. This approach not only prepares you for the complexities of life but also enriches your growth journey. Embracing this balanced perspective can lead to a more authentic, fulfilled life, where challenges are met with resilience and opportunities are pursued with realistic optimism.

The Danger of Toxic Positivity: Accepting Negative Emotions as Part of Growth

In pursuing a contented life, it's common to encounter the mantra "stay positive" as a proposed panacea for all of life's complexities. However, when this well-meaning advice morphs into a relentless drive to maintain a cheerful facade regardless of genuine feelings, it can become what is known as toxic positivity. This is the excessive and ineffective overgeneralization of a happy, optimistic state across all situations—the pressure always to appear happy and positive disregards the authentic human emotional experience. Toxic positivity can invalidate genuine feelings of sadness, grief, or fear, which are essential and typical parts of the human experience. It can create a situation where individuals feel guilty for feeling emotions considered negative or harmful, leading to an emotional dissonance that hinders genuine emotional processing and can exacerbate feelings of isolation and distress.

Emotional authenticity, or acknowledging and expressing a full spectrum of emotions, is crucial for healthy psychological development. It fosters resilience, aids in stress management, and promotes deeper relationships with others. Emotional authenticity involves understanding and expressing one's emotions healthily and appropriately rather than suppressing them. For example, acknowledging and sharing feelings of sadness after a personal loss can lead to more significant emotional relief and open up channels for support and connection with others. It also allows for a more realistic self-perception, which is vital for personal growth and self-awareness.

Developing strategies for expressing and dealing with negative emotions is essential to constructively navigate the complex landscape of human emotions. Journaling, for instance, offers a private, unfiltered medium for expressing thoughts and feelings. This practice can help clarify emotions and lead to insights about underlying feelings and how they influence behavior. Therapy, another powerful tool, provides a structured environment for exploring emotions with a professional. It can help identify patterns in emotional responses and develop strategies for managing emotions more effectively. Emotional regulation techniques such as deep breathing, meditation, or progressive muscle relaxation can also be crucial. These techniques help manage physiological responses to emotions, allowing for a calmer, more measured approach to dealing with feelings that might otherwise feel overwhelming.

Balancing positivity with realism involves acknowledging that life is a medley of diverse experiences and emotions, each adding depth and color. Maintaining a positive outlook is undoubtedly beneficial, but staying grounded in reality is equally important. This balance can be achieved by setting boundaries around positivity. For instance, while looking for the silver lining in difficult situations is helpful, it's also important to recognize when it's necessary to face the reality of a problem directly, without minimization or avoidance. Setting boundaries might mean permitting yourself to feel unhappy or upset about something without immediately trying to counter it with a positive spin. It involves understanding that it's okay not to feel okay sometimes. This does not reflect a failure of positivity but rather a full engagement with the complexity of human life.

In this exploration of toxic positivity, emotional authenticity, and the balance between positivity and realism, we tread the nuanced realities of human emotions. Understanding and implementing these concepts encourages a healthier, more balanced approach to self-help and personal development. It underscores the importance of embracing life's diverse emotional experiences as essential parts of personal growth and human connection.

Debunking the One-Size-Fits-All Solution: Personalizing Your Self-Help Journey

In the vast sea of self-help guidance, there's a frequent assumption that specific strategies are universally effective and applicable to everyone regardless of their unique circumstances, backgrounds, or personal preferences. However, this one-size-fits-all approach can sometimes fail to reach the mark, leaving you feeling the advice doesn't quite resonate or fails to bring about the change you seek. The truth is that personal growth cannot be standardized; it thrives on customization. Everyone brings distinct experiences, strengths, and challenges, making personalization beneficial and necessary for effective self-help.

Self-help strategies often fall short when they need to consider individual differences. For instance, a popular book might advocate waking up at 5 a.m. as a cornerstone of successful routines; however, if you're a night owl whose creativity and productivity peak in the evening, this advice contradicts your natural rhythm. Similarly, methods that work wonders for one person might feel completely unnatural or ineffective for another due to differences in personality, lifestyle, or specific mental health needs. Recognizing these nuances is crucial; it empowers you to seek out and adapt strategies that align closely with your personal attributes and life situation, enhancing the likelihood of sustainable success.

The Role of Personalization in Self-Help

Personalization in self-help involves tailoring strategies to fit your unique psychological makeup, life circumstances, and personal preferences. This bespoke approach increases the effectiveness of self-help techniques and makes the process more engaging and less of a chore. When advice feels relevant and closely aligned with your individual needs, you're far more likely to commit to it and see tangible results. For example, suppose you're more motivated by group settings rather than solo activities. In that case, choosing group fitness classes or study groups over individual sessions can drastically improve your chances of sticking with these habits.

To effectively personalize your self-help journey, start by understanding your personality traits, strengths, and weaknesses. Tools like the Myers-Briggs Type Indicator or the StrengthsFinder can provide valuable insights into your attributes, guiding you in choosing strategies that match your strengths. For instance, strategies involving social support or team collaboration are especially effective if you discover you're particularly good at empathizing with others.

Assessment and Self-Reflection

Assessment and self-reflection are foundational in the personalization process. They involve taking a step back to critically evaluate your current state, including your goals, emotional health, and the effectiveness of your current strategies. This introspective look helps identify what works for you and doesn't, facilitating a more tailored approach to self-help. Simple tools like journaling can be profoundly effective for this purpose. Regularly writing down your thoughts, reactions, and feelings about various experiences and strategies can uncover patterns in what enhances your well-being and what detracts from it.

Reflective practices such as meditation can deepen your understanding of your mental and emotional states, helping you discern the self-help methods most conducive to your growth. For example, if meditation makes you feel significantly more peaceful and focused, incorporating mindfulness-based strategies into your self-help plan might be particularly beneficial.

Creating a Customized Self-Help Plan

Once you clearly understand your needs and preferences, the next step is creating a customized self-help plan. This plan should be dynamic, evolving as you grow and your circumstances change. Start by setting clear, personalized goals that reflect your aspirations and take into account your strengths and limitations. For instance, if you thrive in structured environments, you might set a goal to organize your workspace thoroughly by the end of the month, outlining specific steps and scheduling times to tackle different areas.

Select strategies that resonate with you and align with your attributes. If you're an audio learner, incorporating podcasts or audiobooks into your learning strategies can enhance your engagement and retention of information. Additionally, consider the pacing of your plan. Some people thrive on rapid change, while others require more time to adjust to new habits or routines. Adjust the pacing of your self-help plan to match your comfort level, allowing yourself the flexibility to speed up or slow down as needed.

Regular feedback is crucial in a personalized self-help plan. Set up periodic progress reviews and be open to adjusting your strategies based on the feedback. If a particular approach isn't working, don't hesitate to experiment with alternative methods or tweak existing ones. This iterative process helps refine your plan and deepens your self-understanding, making your self-help journey honestly your own.

By embracing the principles of personalization, assessment, and flexible planning, you can transform your approach to self-help from a generic, possibly frustrating experience into a highly effective, enjoyable journey of personal growth. Tailoring the process to fit your unique personality and life circumstances increases the likelihood of achieving your goals. It makes the path to these goals more aligned with your true self.

The Fallacy of Perpetual Happiness: Embracing Life's Ups and Downs

In today's culture, there's an overwhelming pressure to maintain a facade of constant happiness and satisfaction. With their curated feeds of perfect moments, social media platforms amplify this illusion, making it seem uninterrupted happiness is possible and the norm. However, this notion starkly contrasts the inherently fluctuating nature of human emotions. By its very design, life is a tapestry with myriad feelings, each adding depth and richness to our experiences. It is crucial to understand that the pursuit of non-stop happiness is not only unrealistic but can also detract from the fullness of living a genuinely authentic life.

Emotional fluctuations are a natural and healthy part of being human. Just as the ocean's tides rise and fall, our emotions ebb and flow, influenced by many factors, including personal experiences, interactions with others, and even biological processes. To expect constant happiness is akin to expecting the sea to remain still at all times—it goes against the very laws of nature. Recognizing and accepting the normalcy of experiencing a range of emotions, from joy to sadness, excitement to disappointment, is crucial for developing a healthy perspective on life.

The Value of Adverse Experiences

Adversity, often viewed negatively, is invaluable in fostering growth and resilience. When you face challenges and come through the other side, you better understand your strengths and capabilities and develop a greater appreciation for the spectrum of your emotional experiences. For example, enduring the pain of failure can teach resilience and flexibility, often leading to enhanced success in future endeavors. Similarly, experiencing loss can deepen empathy, increasing your ability to connect with others more profoundly. These experiences shape you, sculpting your character and enriching your understanding of the world.

Resilience, the ability to bounce back from setbacks, is built through confronting and navigating through difficulties, not avoiding them. It involves a dynamic interaction between your environment, personal history, and biological capacities. Building resilience is akin to strengthening a muscle—it grows through use and challenge. By facing adversity head-on, you learn to adapt, which, in turn, enhances your capacity to handle future challenges with greater agility and confidence. This process is critical for personal development and contributes significantly to lasting well-being and fulfillment.

Strategies for Resilience

Developing resilience is a multifaceted endeavor that involves several strategies. First and foremost, cultivating a strong support network is vital. Relationships are the bedrock of psychological resilience. They provide emotional sustenance, practical assistance, and a sense of belonging and purpose. Whether it's family, friends, or community groups, surrounding yourself with supportive people creates a safety net that can catch you when you fall and help lift you back up.

Self-care is another crucial strategy. It includes activities that nurture your physical, mental, and emotional health. This might mean engaging in regular physical activity, which not only improves your physical health but also profoundly affects your mood and mental clarity. It could also involve setting aside time for relaxation and hobbies that bring you joy, ensuring that you recharge and ward off the effects of stress. Maintaining a balanced diet, ensuring adequate sleep, and practicing mindfulness are all essential aspects of a comprehensive self-care regimen.

Gratitude, too, plays a pivotal role in building resilience. By regularly acknowledging and appreciating what you have, rather than fixating on what you lack or what has gone wrong, you cultivate a mindset that values the present and fosters positivity, which can dramatically improve your psychological resilience. Practices such as keeping a gratitude journal or simply taking a moment each day to reflect on things you're grateful for can shift your focus from adversity to appreciation, which enhances your ability to manage life's ups and downs.

Finding Meaning in Struggle

Finally, one of the most profound ways to handle life's lows is by finding meaning in your struggles. Viewing challenges as opportunities for personal growth and learning can transform how you experience adversity. When you start to see your struggles as necessary steps in your personal development, as essential chapters in your life story, they begin to feel less like obstacles and more like integral, meaningful aspects of your journey. This shift in perspective doesn't just help you cope with difficulties; it enriches your life, making your experiences more meaningful and rewarding.

Embracing life's natural ebb and flow, understanding the value of adversity, and employing strategies to build resilience are all crucial for a balanced, fulfilling life. By recognizing the limitations of perpetual happiness and learning to navigate through life's inevitable ups and downs, you equip yourself with the tools to survive and thrive, no matter what life throws your way.

"Follow Your Passion" Isn't Enough: Combining Passion with Practicality

The advice to "follow your passion" has become a staple in career guidance and personal development. It's a message that resonates deeply, suggesting a life where work feels like play and each day is imbued with a sense of purpose. However, while passion is a powerful motivator, it is not a standalone solution; it must be tempered with practicality to ensure personal fulfillment, stability, and sustainability in one's career and life choices.

The Pitfalls of Following Passion Alone

Immersing yourself in work you love is undoubtedly appealing, but an unbridled pursuit of passion can lead to several potential pitfalls. It may lead to financial instability, especially if the passion-driven career path has limited income potential or requires a long period to build profitability. This economic strain can lead to stress and anxiety, undermining the joy your passion was supposed to bring. Additionally, there's the risk of burnout – a state of emotional, physical, and mental exhaustion caused by excessive and prolonged stress. It occurs when you feel overwhelmed, emotionally drained, and unable to meet constant demands. Ironically, pursuing passion without limits can sap the enthusiasm and energy that fueled your passion in the first place, turning what you love into a source of stress instead of joy.

Integrating Passion with Practical Concerns

One must mitigate risks to harness the power of your passion fully; it's crucial to integrate them with practical career and life planning. Identify transferable skills that can link your passion to viable career paths. For instance, if you're passionate about art, skills such as creativity, attention to detail, and innovation are highly transferable to design, advertising, or teaching careers. Conducting market research is another essential step. Understanding the industry landscape related to your passion can help you identify niches with growth potential or oversaturated areas that are more challenging to succeed in. Strategic planning also plays a crucial role; setting clear, actionable goals and developing a step-by-step plan to achieve them can turn the abstract dream of following your passion into a concrete, attainable reality. This might involve additional training, networking to meet influential contacts, or starting part-time while maintaining a stable income source.

The Role of Hard Work and Persistence

Turning a passion into a sustainable career or a fulfilling hobby doesn't happen by chance; it requires hard work, persistence, and adaptability. Success stories often gloss over the years of dedication and relentless effort that lay the groundwork for eventual triumph. Whether revising a manuscript multiple times, enduring countless auditions, or tweaking a business model until it clicks, perseverance in the face of challenges differentiates those who realize their dreams from those who abandon them. Moreover, adaptability is critical as it allows you to pivot and tweak your plans based on feedback and changing circumstances, ensuring your passion can evolve and sustain itself over time.

Finding Balance Between Passion and Realism

Realism does not mean giving up on your dreams; instead, it involves approaching them with a clear-eyed perspective that considers the realities of life. Balancing passion with realism means recognizing the need for a stable income, setting boundaries to prevent burnout, and being willing to adjust your expectations and timelines. It's about finding a middle ground where you can enjoy the fulfillment that comes from doing what you love without sacrificing your well-being or financial security. This balance might look different for everyone; for some, it might mean pursuing passion projects on the side while working a regular job, while for others, it could involve diving into a passion full-time but with a well-thought-out business plan and safety net in place.

By embracing both passion and practicality, you equip yourself to follow your dreams and live them sustainably. Integrating practical steps with pursuing your passions builds a foundation supporting your career and overall happiness and well-being.

As we close this chapter on debunking popular self-help myths, we've uncovered the nuanced truths behind catchy maxims. From the myth of perpetual happiness to the oversimplification of positive thinking and the limits of following passion alone, it's clear that actual personal development requires a balanced, well-rounded approach. As you move forward, remember that real growth involves embracing complexity, acknowledging limitations, and continually adapting strategies to meet the ever-changing demands of life. Let's carry these insights into the next chapter, where we'll explore practical strategies for enhancing communication and relationships, further enriching your journey toward personal development.

Management and Productivity

Imagine, for a moment, the serenity of a well-tended garden, each plant and flower meticulously placed to ensure optimal growth, each pathway clear, inviting you to stroll and admire the blooms. Just as a gardener uses thoughtful planning to enhance the beauty and productivity of a garden, effective time management allows you to cultivate a life where your tasks and goals are as well-arranged as those vibrant beds of flowers. This chapter is dedicated to transforming your everyday jumble of tasks and responsibilities into a well-ordered array that boosts your productivity and peace of mind.

Prioritizing Your To-Do List: Techniques That Work

In the realm of time management, prioritizing what needs to be done is as fundamental as watering is to gardening. Without it, just as plants can wither, so can your chances of achieving your goals. Let's explore some robust methods to help you manage your tasks effectively, ensuring you're both busy and productive.

One of the most renowned techniques for organizing tasks is the Eisenhower Box, a simple yet profound tool for decision-making introduced by Dwight D. Eisenhower. It divides tasks into four categories based on urgency and importance: urgent and important, important but not urgent, urgent but not important, and neither urgent nor important. This method compels you to focus on tasks that contribute to your long-term mission, goals, and values rather than getting caught up in the tyranny of urgent but not necessarily important tasks. For example:

<u>Urgent and Important</u>: These tasks need immediate attention and have significant consequences. An example might be finishing a report due tomorrow.

<u>Important but Not Urgent</u>: These tasks help achieve long-term goals but do not require immediate action. An example is planning a project months in advance.

<u>Urgent but Not Important</u>: These tasks require immediate action but do not contribute to long-term goals, like answering non-essential emails.

<u>Neither Urgent nor Important</u>: These tasks are often distractions, such as browsing social media without purpose.

Another compelling strategy is the ABCDE method, a more nuanced form of task prioritization. Here, you label each of your tasks with a letter: 'A' for very important tasks that have severe consequences if not completed, 'B' for tasks that are somewhat important but have mild consequences, 'C' for tasks that have no consequences whether done or not, 'D' for tasks that can be delegated, and 'E' for tasks that can be eliminated. This method helps prioritize tasks and streamlines your to-do list, ensuring you spend your time and energy on what truly matters.

The Role of Urgency vs. Importance

Understanding the difference between urgent tasks and important tasks is crucial for effective prioritization. Urgent tasks demand immediate attention and are often associated with achieving someone else's goals. They are the ones who shout, "Now!". Important tasks, on the other hand, contribute to long-term missions and objectives. These tasks require more initiative and planning but ensure your growth and fulfillment. The challenge lies in balancing these tasks, as the urgent often overshadows the important. Regularly assessing your tasks through the lens of urgency and importance ensures that your daily activities contribute to your broader life goals rather than just filling your time with busyness.

Daily vs. Long-Term Prioritization

While daily tasks are crucial for maintaining your life's momentum, long-term tasks propel you towards your future. Daily prioritization focuses on tasks that need immediate attention and are often driven by deadlines. In contrast, long-term prioritization is about setting goals that require sustained effort over time, such as completing a professional certification or writing a book. Balancing these requires a conscientious effort to keep the daily urgencies from crowding out time for long-term ambitions. It's about planting seeds for the future, even as you tend to the urgent weeds that sprout daily.

For instance, if your daily priority includes meeting project deadlines (urgent and important), your long-term priority might be attending a course that enhances your skills (important but not urgent). Allocating specific times for both types of tasks ensures that urgent matters are handled while long-term goals are steadily advanced.

Tools and Apps for Prioritization

In today's digital age, numerous tools and apps can assist in organizing and prioritizing your tasks efficiently. Apps like Trello, Asana, and Todoist allow you to create customizable lists and projects, set deadlines, and delegate tasks. These tools can be invaluable for visually organizing tasks and tracking progress. They also often include features that allow you to prioritize tasks using various methods, including color coding or tagging tasks by urgency and importance. Leveraging these tools can help you keep your to-do list manageable and your priorities clear, enabling you to navigate your day efficiently and gracefully.

Trello: This board-based system allows tasks to be categorized and color-coded, making it easy to prioritize at a glance.

Asana: Provides project management features with task dependencies and timelines, helping you see which tasks are critical to moving forward.

Todoist: Focuses on individual task management with options to label tasks by priority and set reminders, ensuring nothing falls through the cracks.

Benefits of Prioritization

Mastering task prioritization allows you to distinguish between what merely demands your attention and what genuinely deserves it. This discernment is critical to managing time effectively and living a life aligned with your deepest values and aspirations. Prioritizing tasks helps reduce stress, improve productivity, and ensure that you are making progress on meaningful goals rather than just staying busy.

By prioritizing effectively, you can allocate your most productive time to tasks requiring high concentration and creativity, leaving less critical tasks for periods when your energy levels might be lower. This strategic time management approach enhances your efficiency and boosts your overall satisfaction and sense of accomplishment.

As we proceed, remember that each task you complete is not just a check off a list but a stepping stone towards the bigger vision you have for your life. By adopting effective prioritization methods, understanding the role of urgency versus importance, balancing daily and long-term priorities, and utilizing modern tools, you can create a robust framework for achieving your goals. This approach ensures that your efforts are not just about staying busy but about making meaningful progress toward your aspirations.

The Myth of Multitasking: Focusing on Single-Tasking for Greater Efficiency

In today's fast-paced world, multitasking is often celebrated as a hallmark of efficiency. It's common to see someone typing on a laptop, responding to texts on their phone, sipping coffee, and glancing at a TV screen simultaneously. This scene is often praised as the pinnacle of productivity. However, recent studies reveal a starkly different narrative. Multitasking, especially when it involves complex tasks, can reduce productivity and increase errors. The human brain is optimized to focus intensely on one task at a time, and when forced to switch attention, the transition isn't seamless. Each switch involves a cost—time lost as the brain realigns its focus. According to research from the American Psychological Association, this juggling act can lead to as much as a 40% loss in productivity. Moreover, this constant shifting can increase stress levels and burnout, making multitasking less of an asset and more of a liability.

The Benefits of Single-Tasking

The benefits of single-tasking, on the other hand, are manifold. When you focus on one task at a time, your attention isn't fragmented, which leads to greater concentration and better quality of work. For instance, if you dedicate a block of time to developing a presentation without the interruption of emails and phone calls, you're likely to produce a more coherent and creative work product. Single-tasking allows for deeper engagement with your task, fostering a richer understanding and mastery of the content. Furthermore, this focused approach often leads to quicker completion times as you aren't constantly regaining lost ground due to interruptions.

Additionally, single-tasking can significantly lower stress levels. When you're not perpetually pulled in multiple directions, you feel a greater sense of control and accomplishment, contributing to higher job satisfaction and mental well-being. You can immerse yourself fully in one activity, leading to a state of flow where productivity and creativity peak. This immersive state is challenging to achieve when your attention is divided among various tasks.

Strategies for Embracing Single-Tasking

Adopting a single-tasking approach might be challenging, especially in an environment that mistakenly equates busyness with productivity. However, several strategies can facilitate this transition:

<u>Time Blocking</u>: This involves dedicating specific blocks of time to different tasks and respecting these blocks as you would a meeting with a colleague. For example, you might block the first hour of your workday for deep, creative work and another segment for responding to emails. During each block, all your energy and attention are directed at one task. Tools like the 'Focus Mode' on digital calendars can be invaluable to support this method, signaling to others when you are unavailable.

<u>Minimizing Distractions</u>: This goes beyond silencing your phone or closing your email application. It involves creating a physical and digital environment that supports deep work.

Physically, this might mean organizing your workspace to reduce clutter, which can subconsciously pull your attention away from the task at hand. Digitally, consider using apps that block distracting websites during work hours. Creating barriers to multitasking makes it easier to commit to single-tasking.

<u>Setting Clear Boundaries</u>: Creating a single-tasking environment involves more than just physical adjustments; it's about cultivating a mindset that values depth over breadth. This can be encouraged by setting clear expectations with colleagues and family about your availability. Communicate when you focus on solo work and when you are available for discussions and meetings. This helps manage others' expectations and bolsters your commitment to single-tasking, as the designated times become a pact you've made with yourself and others.

<u>Implementing the Pomodoro Technique</u>: This time management method involves working for a set period (usually 25 minutes) followed by a short break (5 minutes). This technique helps maintain focus and prevents burnout, as the breaks provide a mental reset, allowing you to return to your task with renewed energy and concentration.

<u>Prioritizing Tasks</u>: Use prioritization methods like the Eisenhower Matrix or the ABCDE method to identify which tasks require your immediate attention and which can be deferred, delegated, or eliminated. By focusing on high-priority tasks one at a time, you ensure that your efforts are aligned with your most important goals.

<u>Mindfulness and Meditation</u>: Practicing mindfulness and meditation can enhance your ability to focus on a single task. These practices train your mind to stay present, reducing the tendency to get distracted by multiple thoughts or external stimuli. Incorporating mindfulness exercises into your daily routine can significantly improve your concentration and overall productivity.

Creating a Productive Environment

The environment you create is not just about the physical but also the psychological space. It should affirm your deep focus and efficiency goals, turning the space into a sanctuary of productivity.

<u>Physical Adjustments:</u> Ensure your workspace is clean and organized. A clutter-free environment reduces distractions and promotes focus. Arrange your desk so everything you need is within reach, minimizing the need to get up and break your concentration.

<u>Digital Adjustments</u>: Customize your computer and phone settings to minimize interruptions. Turn off non-essential notifications and use apps that help you stay focused. For example, apps like StayFocusd or Freedom can block distracting websites during work hours.

<u>Psychological Adjustments:</u> Cultivate a mindset that values single-tasking. Remind yourself that depth and quality of work are more important than the sheer quantity of tasks completed. Practice self-compassion and avoid self-criticism if you struggle with single-tasking initially. Over time, it will become more natural and beneficial.

Observing the Impact

As you incorporate these practices into your daily routine, observe the changes in your work output, stress levels, and job satisfaction. You'll likely find that single-tasking enhances your productivity and enriches your professional and personal life. You may notice that tasks are completed more efficiently and to a higher standard and that your overall sense of well-being improves as you experience less stress and more satisfaction in your accomplishments.

The myth of multitasking has been debunked by numerous studies showing that it is less effective than focusing on one task at a time. Embracing single-tasking not only boosts productivity but also enhances the quality of work and reduces stress. By implementing strategies like time blocking, minimizing distractions, setting clear boundaries, using the Pomodoro Technique, prioritizing tasks, and practicing mindfulness, you can transition to a more effective and fulfilling way of working. Creating an environment that supports physical and psychological single-tasking will further reinforce your commitment to this approach. As you observe the positive impact of single-tasking on your life, you'll be motivated to continue refining and improving your methods for greater efficiency and satisfaction.

Overcoming Distractions in a Digital World

In this age of information overload, where the ding of a notification can pull us out of deep work and into a vortex of emails, social media, and instant messaging, managing digital distractions has become crucial for maintaining productivity The landscape of our digital interactions is vast and varied, making it a fertile ground for distractions that can disrupt our focus and flow Let's explore how you can identify these digital distractions and implement strategies to regain control of your attention, ensuring that technology serves you rather than derails you.

Identifying Common Digital Distractions

The first step in mastering your digital environment is identifying what specific aspects are pulling your focus away. Common culprits include social media notifications, which tempt us with the promise of social connection and instant updates but often lead to prolonged scrolling sessions. Email alerts can also disrupt your workflow, creating a sense of urgency around messages that frequently do not require immediate attention. Additionally, app notifications from news outlets, games, or productivity tools can fragment your concentration, pulling your mind in multiple directions. By thoroughly auditing your digital habits, you can pinpoint which applications and behaviors fragment your focus the most. This might involve observing your behavior over a few days or using digital monitoring tools that provide insights into your most frequented sites and apps. Awareness is the precursor to change; in this case, it sets the stage for you to make informed decisions about managing your digital interactions.

Setting Digital Boundaries

Once you've identified your digital distractions, setting boundaries that help you manage these effectively is the next step. This involves creating rules that govern when and how you engage with technology. For instance, you may turn off social media notifications during work hours or schedule specific times to check your email, such as mid-morning and late afternoon. This approach helps to contain potential distractions within designated times, preventing them from bleeding into periods dedicated to focused work. In addition, you can use features like "Do Not Disturb" or "Focus Mode" on your devices to minimize interruptions. These tools allow you to silence notifications for a set period, making it easier to maintain your focus. Setting boundaries with your digital devices isn't just about reducing interruptions; it's about reclaiming your attention and directing it toward tasks that align with your goals and values.

Using Technology Mindfully

While technology can be a source of distraction, when used mindfully, it has the potential to enhance productivity. Mindful use of technology involves engaging with digital tools intentionally, ensuring that each interaction has a clear purpose and contributes positively to your workflow. For example, before opening your email or a social media app, take a moment to ask yourself what your intention is. Are you checking your email to clear urgent tasks, or are you looking to distract yourself from a challenging assignment? Pausing and questioning can help you make more conscious choices about technology use. Additionally, consider using technology to support your focus, such as listening to white noise or instrumental music that can enhance concentration or using apps that promote productivity through structured work intervals and breaks.

Tools to Block Distractions

To further support your efforts in managing digital distractions, numerous tools and apps are designed to help you maintain focus. Software like Cold Turkey or Freedom can block distracting websites and apps entirely or allow you to set specific times for restricted use. These tools can be handy during work sessions that require deep concentration, such as writing, coding, or designing. Another helpful tool is a website blocker, which can prevent accidental detours onto time-wasting sites. Customizing these tools to fit your needs and working style allows you to create a digital environment that fosters rather than fractures your focus.

Navigating the digital landscape with intention and control empowers you to use technology as a tool for productivity, not procrastination. You create a framework that supports sustained concentration and efficiency by identifying distractions, setting firm boundaries, using technology mindfully, and employing tools to maintain focus. As we continue integrating technology into every aspect of our lives, mastering these skills becomes beneficial and essential for anyone looking to thrive in an increasingly connected world.

Setting Boundaries for Better Time Management

Understanding the importance of setting boundaries is akin to knowing how to draw lines on a map that define one territory from another. In the vast landscape of your daily life, clear boundaries—those invisible lines—help delineate where your responsibilities begin and end, and they signal to others how you expect to be treated and what you are willing to tolerate. Setting boundaries is not about isolation; instead, it's about creating healthy limits that enable you to manage your time more effectively and interact with others respectfully and productively. It's crucial in both personal and professional realms because it helps prevent burnout and reduces the likelihood of tasks and social demands infringing upon your time and space.

For instance, in a professional setting, a well-defined boundary could be not checking emails after work hours. This ensures that your time is protected and conditions others not to expect instant responses at all hours, thereby setting a standard for communication. In personal settings, it might mean allocating specific times for family or recreational activities, during which work-related tasks are not allowed to intrude. This helps maintain a healthy work-life balance, which is crucial for long-term productivity and well-being.

Techniques for Boundary Setting

Effectively setting and communicating boundaries requires clarity, consistency, and respect for yourself and others. Start by clearly identifying your limits. This involves understanding what you can allow and accept and what makes you uncomfortable or stressed. For example, if starting your day with immediate task requests causes stress, you might set a boundary to have the first hour of your workday as uninterrupted planning time.

Once your boundaries are defined, communicating them clearly and assertively is vital. This doesn't mean being aggressive or inflexible but being honest and direct. Suppose you decide not to take work calls during weekends. Communicating this clearly to your colleagues and clients—as early as possible, preferably before you're directly confronted with the situation—helps set expectations and reduces misunderstandings. It's also helpful to explain the rationale behind your boundaries; this can increase understanding and support from those around you.

These conversations can be challenging, especially if you're not used to asserting yourself this way. It can be beneficial to practice what you want to say beforehand or even role-play the scenario with a friend or family member. This preparation can make the actual conversation feel more comfortable and natural.

Balancing Flexibility with Firmness

While it's essential to be firm in maintaining your boundaries to protect your time and well-being, it's equally important to remain flexible enough to adapt to exceptional circumstances or emergencies. Balancing this flexibility with firmness is a nuanced aspect of setting boundaries. For instance, an exception might be made during a critical project phase or emergency if you have a no-work-calls-after-hours rule.

The key here is to ensure these exceptions do not become the rule. When exceptions arise, clearly communicate why you are making them and that they are temporary. This helps prevent setting a precedent that erodes your boundaries over time. Additionally, after the need for flexibility has passed, reassert your original boundaries to ensure they continue to be respected.

Respecting Others' Boundaries

Just as you set and enforce your boundaries, it's vital to respect the boundaries that others have in place. This reciprocal respect builds more robust, cooperative relationships with colleagues, friends, and family. Paying attention to and honoring other people's limits shows that you value their well-being and autonomy. For example, if a coworker has specified they do not work on weekends unless in cases of emergencies, respecting this boundary without pushing for exceptions builds trust and mutual respect.

In scenarios where you are unsure about someone's boundaries, it's always better to ask rather than assume. This prevents potential oversteps and demonstrates your respect for their preferences and needs. By fostering an environment where boundaries are mutually respected, you contribute to a culture of empathy and consideration, significantly enhancing collective harmony and productivity.

In essence, setting boundaries is an ongoing process of defining what works best for you and balancing that with the needs and expectations of those around you. It requires awareness, clear communication, and a willingness to uphold one's defined limits, all essential for effective time management and healthy relationships. As you continue advancing through the complexities of personal and professional interactions, remember that well-set boundaries are not barriers but expressions of respect for your time and others, facilitating a more organized, respectful, and productive life.

The Pomodoro Technique: A Timer-Based Approach to Productivity

In the quest for productivity, the Pomodoro Technique stands out as a straightforward yet effective tool that harnesses the power of focused time intervals to enhance efficiency and reduce the anxiety often associated with task completion. Developed in the late

1980s by Francesco Cirillo, the technique derives its name from the Italian word for 'tomato,' inspired by the tomato-shaped kitchen timer Cirillo used as a university student to track his work sessions. At its core, the Pomodoro Technique works in short, intensely focused bursts of 25 minutes, followed by a five-minute break. These intervals are known as 'Pomodoros.' After completing four Pomodoros, you take a longer break of about 15 to 30 minutes. This rhythm helps maintain high concentration levels and ensures that your brain gets the rest it needs to stay sharp and creative.

Explaining the Pomodoro Technique

The brilliance of the Pomodoro Technique lies in its simplicity and the psychological benefits it offers. Each 25-minute work session is short enough to sustain urgency and focus but not so long that it leads to burnout. This pacing taps into the brain's capacity for sprinting, where focus can be maintained at a high level without distractions. The subsequent short breaks serve as a critical recovery period, allowing your mind to reset and refresh, which is essential for maintaining long-term productivity throughout the day. In addition, the technique helps manage the feeling of being overwhelmed by large tasks or projects. By breaking work down into manageable intervals, tasks become less daunting, progress becomes more tangible, and momentum builds with each completed Pomodoro.

Implementing the Technique

To integrate the Pomodoro Technique into your daily routine:

1. Start by identifying a task or a series of tasks you wish to accomplish.

2. Set your Pomodoro timer for 25 minutes and commit to working entirely on the task until the timer rings.

3. Resist all interruptions and temptations to shift your focus.

4. Once the session ends, mark one Pomodoro complete and take a five-minute break.

This break is your time to step away from your desk, stretch, grab a cup of tea, or close your eyes and breathe. After every four Pomodoros, take a more extended break to disengage from work fully. This helps prevent fatigue and keeps your mind sharp and efficient.

As simple as it sounds, implementing this technique requires discipline and commitment. It's tempting to skip breaks when you're in the flow of work, but the structure of the Pomodoro Technique is designed to maximize your productivity by balancing work and rest. Adherence to the specified intervals is crucial for the technique to be effective.

Customizing the Technique

While the traditional Pomodoro Technique prescribes 25-minute work intervals, one size does not fit all regarding productivity. Depending on the nature of your work or your attention span, slightly longer or shorter periods work better for you. Some may thrive on 30-minute intervals with longer breaks, while others might prefer shorter sessions of 20 minutes. Experiment with different timings to find your optimal work-break ratio.

The tasks suited to the Pomodoro Technique can vary. It is most effective with tasks requiring sustained mental effort, like writing, coding, or studying. However, longer intervals might be necessary for tasks needing open-ended creative thinking or deep problem-solving to fully engage with the work without disrupting the thought process.

Tools and Apps to Support the Technique

Numerous digital tools and apps can enhance your experience and aid in implementing the Pomodoro Technique. Pomodoro timers are available as desktop apps, web-based tools, and mobile apps, many of which allow you to customize the length of work and break periods according to your preferences. Apps like Focus Keeper, Tomato Timer, and Pomodoro not only keep track of your Pomodoros but also allow you to record what you accomplished in each interval, providing a sense of progress and a log of how you've spent your time. Some apps even offer features like blocking distracting websites during work intervals and integrating the best productivity techniques to keep you focused and efficient.

Incorporating the Pomodoro Technique into your workday introduces a structured, disciplined approach to managing time that can dramatically enhance your productivity and reduce work-related stress. Working with time—not against it—helps you take control of your schedule efficiently and sustainably, allowing for periods of high focus and necessary rest. As you continue to adapt this method to your personal and professional life, you may find it becomes an indispensable part of your toolkit for achieving efficiency and fulfilling your potential in your endeavors.

De-clutter Your Space, De-clutter Your Mind: The Link Between Organization and Productivity

In today's fast-paced world, maintaining productivity is a challenge many face. One often overlooked aspect that significantly affects productivity is the state of our physical environment. The connection between a cluttered space and a cluttered mind is well-documented, and understanding this relationship can lead to enhanced efficiency, focus, and overall well-being. This concept is rooted in the principles of environmental psychology, which examines how our surroundings influence our mental states and behaviors. The state of our physical and digital habitats can profoundly influence our mental clarity and productivity. A cluttered space can mirror and even exacerbate a cluttered mind, leading to decreased efficiency and increased stress. Conversely, a clean and organized environment can facilitate clearer thinking and a smoother workflow, making the task of de-cluttering a physical act and a mental refresh.

The Psychological Benefits of a Clutter-Free Space

Numerous psychological studies support the relationship between a clutter-free environment and mental clarity. A cluttered space is visually distracting; it can take your attention away from tasks requiring focus, diminishing your cognitive resources. This constant, often subconscious, visual noise can lead to increased anxiety and decreased concentration. On the other hand, a clean space can enhance your ability to process information and focus on the tasks at hand. Organizing your space can also give you a sense of control and accomplishment, boosting mood and productivity. In addition, de-cluttering can be therapeutic—removing physical items that no longer serve you can also help in letting go of mental burdens, leading to a lighter, more focused state of mind.

Steps to De-cluttering Your Workspace

Effectively de-cluttering your workspace requires a systematic approach, starting with removing all unnecessary items. Begin by emptying your workspace, then reintroduce items one at a time, starting with the essentials—those tools and documents you use daily. For each item you consider returning to your desk or office, ask yourself whether it serves a functional purpose or brings you joy. If the answer is neither, it probably doesn't belong in your workspace. Next, implement effective storage solutions. Use drawers, files, and organizational trays to keep necessary items accessible but out of sight. Labeling these storage spaces can further enhance efficiency, helping you find what you need quickly without unnecessary searchin. For paperwork, adopt a system to keep your desk clear, such as a file organizer where incoming and outgoing documents are easily accessible.

Maintaining an Organized Space

Regular maintenance is critical to keeping your workspace clutter-free. Set a weekly or bi-weekly schedule to re-evaluate your space, removing any items that have accumulated without a purpose and reorganizing as needed to ensure everything remains in its place. This regular upkeep keeps your space functional and reinforces the habit of maintaining organization Integrate organizational upkeep into your routine to ensure your workspace remains a haven of productivity This might involve a brief daily cleanup at the end of your workday, where you restore items to their designated places, file away papers, and clear your desk for the next day Such habits prepare your space for immediate use the next morning and provide a psychological cue to your brain that the workday has ended, promoting better work-life balance.

De-cluttering extends beyond the physical into the digital realm. Digital clutter, including disorganized desktops, overflowing inboxes, and indiscriminately saved files, can be just as distracting and overwhelming as physical mess. Start by cleaning up your digital files—organize them into clearly labeled folders and delete anything that is no longer relevant Email can be a significant source of digital clutter Regularly unsubscribing from unnecessary newsletters and setting up filters to organize incoming emails automatically can keep your inbox manageable For ongoing digital maintenance, dedicate weekly time to review and arrange your digital files and emails This keeps your digital workspace clear and helps you stay familiar with your content, reducing the time spent searching for files in the future.

By embracing de-cluttering principles, physically and digitally, you create an environment that reflects and supports your mental clarity and productivity. This clean, well-organized space enhances your focus and efficiency and contributes to a more serene and controlled mental state, helping you tackle your tasks confidently and calmly.

Start Small Begin the de-cluttering process by tackling small areas. Focus on one drawer, shelf, or corner of your desk at a time. This approach prevents feelings of overwhelm and allows you to see immediate progress, motivating you to continue.

Categorize and Prioritize Sort your items into categories: keep, discard, and relocate. Prioritize keeping items that are essential and frequently used. Discard items that are broken, outdated, or no longer serve a purpose. Relocate items that belong in other areas of your home or office.

Create Functional Zones Designate specific areas for different activities. For example, create a dedicated workspace for tasks requiring deep focus, a relaxation area for breaks, and a storage area for supplies. This zoning helps maintain order and ensures that items are easily accessible when needed. Embrace minimalism in your workspace decor. While personal touches can make a space feel comforting and inspiring, too many can become distractions Choose meaningful items, like photos or motivational quotes, and avoid overcrowding your desk with knick-knacks. This balance keeps your space personal and motivating without contributing to visual clutter.

Implement Storage Solutions Invest in storage solutions that suit your needs. Use shelves, bins, and drawer organizers to keep items neatly stored and easily accessible   Labeling storage containers can further enhance organization and streamline your workflow. Successfully de-cluttering and organizing your space provides a sense of accomplishment. This achievement boosts your self-esteem and motivation, creating a positive feedback loop that enhances your overall productivity and well-being. As we wrap up this exploration of de-cluttering and its profound impact on productivity, we see how a clean environment is more than just aesthetically pleasing—it's a cornerstone of effective work habits and mental clarity. De-cluttering your space is more than just a physical task; it's a transformative process that can significantly impact your mental and emotional well-being. This chapter has equipped you with strategies to create and maintain an organized space, setting the stage for enhanced productivity and reduced stress. Moving forward, these principles of organization and clarity will dovetail into our subsequent discussion on mindset and personal development, where we'll explore how internal states and attitudes further influence our productivity and overall life satisfaction.

Mindset and Personal Development

As dawn breaks over the horizon, painting the sky with hues of orange and pink, so does the realization of our potential with each new day. Our mindset profoundly influences how we perceive challenges, absorb knowledge, and adapt to change. This chapter examines the fertile ground of our mental frameworks, exploring how cultivating a growth mindset can transform the ordinary into the extraordinary in personal and professional areas. The distinction between a growth mindset and a fixed mindset can significantly impact every aspect of our lives, from learning and personal development to career success and relationships. By understanding these mindsets and actively working to cultivate a growth mindset, we can unlock our potential, overcome challenges, and achieve greater success and fulfillment. Embracing a growth mindset fosters resilience, persistence, and a lifelong love for learning, empowering us to continuously evolve and reach new heights. Here, you'll learn not only to adjust your sails in the face of gusty winds but to embrace the gales as vital to your journey of growth and development.

Cultivating a Growth Mindset: The Path to Continuous Improvement

Understanding Growth vs. Fixed Mindset

The concept of mindsets, particularly the distinction between a growth mindset and a fixed mindset, has gained significant attention in educational psychology and personal development. Introduced by psychologist Carol Dweck in her book *Mindset: The New Psychology of Success*, this theory explains how our beliefs about our abilities and intelligence can profoundly influence our behavior, learning, and overall success in life. In a fixed mindset, individuals believe their abilities, intelligence, and talents are static traits; they have a certain amount, and that's it. This perspective can lead to a desire to appear intelligent, with every encounter being judged and every mistake directly reflecting their capabilities. People with a fixed mindset may shy away from challenges, fearing failure will expose their perceived limitations. They often avoid situations where they might fail, missing out on opportunities for growth and development.

Conversely, a growth mindset thrives on challenge and sees failures not as evidence of unintelligence but as springboards for growth and stretching existing abilities. The effort is not seen as fruitless but as the path to mastery. People with a growth mindset understand that intelligence and talent can be developed through dedication and hard work. They embrace challenges, persist through obstacles, learn from criticism, and find inspiration in others' success. This mindset fosters a love of learning and resilience essential for significant accomplishments.

The Impact on Performance and Fulfillment

This dichotomy affects not only performance but also personal and professional fulfillment. For instance, adopting a growth mindset can lead to a deeper engagement in tasks, a greater love of learning, and resilience in the face of setbacks—indispensable qualities in today's ever-evolving world. When you believe that you can develop your abilities through dedication and hard work, every challenge becomes an opportunity to grow, every critique a lesson to learn from, and every success a milestone in the journey of self-improvement.

A growth mindset enables individuals to:

Embrace Challenges: Individuals with a growth mindset view challenges as opportunities to improve and develop their skills rather than threats to their intelligence. They are more likely to persist in the face of setbacks and will make the necessary effort to overcome obstacles. Persist in the Face of Setbacks: Understanding that failure is a natural part of the learning process and a stepping stone to success. A growth mindset leads to a constructive response to misstep instead of seeing failure as a reflection of their inherent abilities. Learn from **Criticism**: Seeing feedback as valuable information that can help them improve. A growth mindset encourages individuals to seek out and value constructive criticism, viewing it as an essential tool for improvement. Find **Inspiration in Others' Success**: Using others' achievements as motivation to enhance their own abilities. They believe that others' achievements demonstrate what is possible with hard work and dedication. Strategies for Developing a Growth Mindset

Cultivating a growth mindset involves conscious efforts and deliberate actions. Here are some strategies to help develop this mindset:

Embrace Challenges Wholeheartedly: When faced with a daunting task, instead of recoiling in fear of failure, use it as an opportunity to expand your skills. Each effort, each struggle, and each act of persistence are stepping stones to higher proficiency and deeper understanding. For example, if you're learning a new language, rather than avoiding speaking for fear of making mistakes, actively engage in conversations to improve your fluency.

Learn from Criticism: Constructive criticism can be a gift wrapped in the guise of tough love. It provides direct points of improvement, offering a clear path to betterment. Instead of defending against feedback, dissect it for growth opportunities and act on it to refine your abilities. For instance, if you receive critical feedback on a project at work, analyze the points raised, identify areas for improvement, and apply the lessons to future projects.

Celebrate the Success of Others: In a fixed mindset, peers' success can often incite envy or a sense of inadequacy. In a growth mindset, however, such success is inspirational. It serves as a motivator, a living testament to the possibilities that await on the other side of dedication and perseverance. Let the achievements of others expand your view of what's possible and propel you to expand your horizons. For example, instead of feeling threatened by a colleague's promotion, view it as evidence that hard work and determination pay off and let it inspire you to pursue your own goals with renewed vigor.

Practice Self-Compassion: Be kind to yourself when you encounter setbacks. Understand that everyone makes mistakes and that these are opportunities to learn and grow. Self-compassion helps maintain motivation and resilience, even when things don't go as planned. For instance, if you fail a test, rather than beating yourself up, acknowledge the effort you put in, identify areas for improvement, and develop a plan to do better next time. Be self-aware; Recognize your current mindset and understand how it influences your thoughts and behaviors. **Set Process-Oriented Goals**: Focus on goals related to the process rather than the outcome. This shift helps you appreciate the learning journey and reduces the fear of failure. For example, instead of setting a goal to "get an A in math," set a goal to "study math for an hour each day." This approach emphasizes effort and learning, fostering a growth mindset.

Adopt a Lifelong Learning Attitude: Commit to continuous learning and self-improvement. Take up new hobbies, read widely, attend workshops, and stay curious. This attitude reinforces the belief that abilities can be enhanced and encourages ongoing personal and professional development.

Individuals can unlock their full potential by understanding the distinctions between a fixed and a growth mindset and actively working to adopt a growth mindset; your shift in perspective not only enhances performance and productivity but also leads to greater personal and professional fulfillment. As you cultivate a growth mindset, remember that every effort counts and every challenge is an opportunity to grow.

The Role of Perseverance

Perseverance is the steadfast effort to do or achieve something despite difficulties, failures, or opposition. It's the gritty determination that underpins a growth mindset. With a belief in personal development, perseverance becomes more than grinding through challenges; it becomes a dynamic journey of learning and adaptation. Your challenges are no longer roadblocks but intriguing problems to solve and learn from. This shift in perception makes perseverance more palatable and effective, fueled by optimism and a proactive stance toward obstacles.

Growth Mindset in Professional Settings

In professional realms, a growth mindset can transform the landscape of work and innovation. It encourages a culture where challenges are welcomed, failures are viewed as teachable moments, and employees' potential is nurtured. For leaders, fostering a growth mindset within teams can lead to more significant innovation, agility, and overall performance. It cultivates an environment where employees feel valued for their outputs and capability to learn and evolve.

Implementing a growth mindset in the workplace involves modeling this mindset through leadership. When leaders openly discuss their failures and the lessons learned, they set a precedent for transparency and continuous improvement. Training programs that focus not only on skill development but also on developing a growth mindset can equip employees with the resilience and adaptability needed in today's fast-paced business world.

Cultivating a growth mindset is a journey worth embarking on, whether to enrich your personal life or enhance your professional environment. It opens up a world where the quest for knowledge never ceases, challenges are met with courage, and the learning process is as celebrated as the victories it leads to.

Resilience in the Face of Failure: Learning from Mistakes

The notion of failure often carries a weight of negativity, a shadow that looms over potential risks and daring ventures. However, what if we shift our perspective to see failure not as a mark of defeat but as a vital ingredient in the recipe for success? This reframing is crucial, not just for personal growth but as a foundational strategy for building resilience. When you start to view each mistake as a stepping stone rather than a stumbling block, you unlock a more forgiving and constructive approach to challenges. Imagine a scenario where you've missed a crucial deadline at work. Instead of spiraling into self-criticism, dissect the situation to understand what went wrong and why. Was it poor time management or perhaps an unrealistic workload? Each insight offers a valuable lesson, turning a moment of failure into a potential future victory.

Building resilience through these experiences is akin to tempering steel; every exposure to the heat of challenges and the hammering of setbacks makes you stronger and more durable. Consider the process of learning a new skill, like playing a guitar. The initial stages are often fraught with discordant notes and awkward hand positions. Each mistake, however, contributes to your understanding of music and finger placement, gradually enhancing your ability to play seamlessly. Over time, what once caused frustration becomes a source of joy and pride. This transformation is resilience in action—growing through what you go through.

Real-life examples of resilience abound and serve as powerful reminders of human tenacity and adaptability. Take the story of a young entrepreneur whose first startup venture failed spectacularly. Instead of retreating from the entrepreneurial scene, they analyzed the collapse to pinpoint exactly where their business model went awry. Armed with this hard-earned knowledge, they launched a new venture addressing these shortcomings, leading to a successful business. This narrative underscores that resilience isn't about avoiding failure; it's about having the courage to try again, equipped with lessons from past defeats.

To actively cultivate resilience, consider engaging in reflective journaling. This practice involves writing down recent failures and objectively identifying what went wrong, what you learned, and how you can adapt your approach in the future. Begin by jotting down a recent instance where things didn't go as planned. Describe the situation with as much neutrality as possible. Next, ask yourself: What can this experience teach me? What skills do I need to develop to handle similar situations better in the future? This exercise not only aids in processing emotions associated with failure but also transforms them into actionable insights, fortifying your resilience for future challenges.

Embracing this restructured view of failure and actively learning from setbacks paves the way for a life characterized by resilience and continual growth. Rather than fearing failure, anticipate the lessons it brings. Each mistake is a dialogue, an opportunity to engage deeply with your actions and their outcomes, ensuring that every misstep informs a more skilled and resilient stride forward.

The Power of Self-Reflection: Learning to Pause and Evaluate

Self-reflection is akin to stepping back from a painting; it allows you to see the entire picture, understand the interplay of colors, and realize that what seems like arbitrary strokes is part of a larger, purposeful design. Similarly, in the canvas of life, self-reflection enables you to step back, assess your experiences, and understand their significance in shaping who you are and who you aspire to become. This process is fundamental to personal growth as it fosters a profound self-awareness, allowing you to recognize patterns in your thoughts and behaviors, understand your motivations, and discern areas needing change or development.

The art of self-reflection is not just about looking back with a critical eye but about doing so with the intent to learn and adapt. When you reflect, you engage in an honest dialogue with yourself. This might involve examining a recent event that didn't go as planned or a conversation that left you unsettled. By dissecting these moments, you can uncover underlying beliefs or assumptions that may steer your reactions and decisions, sometimes subconsciously. For instance, if a failed presentation leads you to avoid future public speaking opportunities, reflection could reveal a deep-seated fear of judgment that might hold you back professionally. Recognizing such patterns is the first step towards transformative change, enabling you to tackle the symptoms of your challenges and their roots.

Methods for Effective Self-Reflection

Several methods can help you make self-reflection effective and a regular part of your routine. Journaling stands out as a potent tool. By writing down your thoughts and experiences, you give them form and substance, making it easier to analyze and understand them. Start with daily entries that describe what happened during your day, how you felt about these events, and why you think you felt that way. Over time, you'll see patterns and triggers, providing valuable insights into your habits and behaviors.

Meditation is another impactful method of reflection that involves introspection and mindfulness. It lets you clear your mind of daily clutter and focus inwardly, promoting calm awareness. During meditation, you can reflect on specific aspects of your life or decisions you need to make, approaching these thoughts with a clear, focused mind that is more receptive to deeper insights.

Feedback analysis is also crucial. This involves revisiting feedback you've received, whether from peers, mentors, or even personal relationships. Analyze this feedback for common themes or areas of concern. This can highlight aspects of your behavior or skills that you may not have recognized as needing improvement, offering another perspective on your personal and professional growth.

Creating a Routine for Self-Reflection

To make self-reflection a consistent part of your life, it's essential to establish it as a routine. This could mean setting aside a specific time each day or week for this practice. Early mornings or late evenings provide the quiet needed for adequate reflection. Treat this time as a sacred appointment with yourself, free from distractions like the internet or phone calls. It's helpful to create a comfortable space dedicated to this practice, whether a particular chair by a window or a small desk arranged with items that inspire calm and focus, such as a plant, a candle, or a piece of art.

Using Reflection to Inform Future Actions

Self-reflection's ultimate goal is to understand yourself better and use that understanding to guide your future actions. This means taking the insights from reflection and translating them into concrete personal and professional development steps. If reflection reveals that you struggle with public speaking, you might take a course on effective communication or join a local Toastmasters club to improve this skill. If you are often harsh in your self-judgment, you might work on cultivating self-compassion through affirmations or therapy.

In every instance, the key is to move from insight to action. This helps you address areas for improvement and reinforces the value of the reflection process by linking it directly to personal growth and enhanced well-being. As you continue to engage in this reflective practice, you'll find that it enriches your understanding of yourself and empowers you to lead a more intentional and fulfilled life, where every experience is an opportunity for growth and every challenge a stepping stone to greater wisdom.

Redefining Vulnerability

Embracing Vulnerability as a Strength

In a society that often equates vulnerability with weakness, there lies a profound misunderstanding of its true essence and power. Vulnerability is not about weakness; it is about the courage to show up and be seen, to share one's true self, and to engage genuinely with others without hiding behind a facade of invulnerability. It involves exposing one's thoughts, feelings, and fears in ways that can feel incredibly daunting, yet it is precisely this openness that paves the way for greater authenticity and connection. By redefining vulnerability as a strength, we begin to see it not as a liability but as a courageous engagement with life that enriches our understanding of ourselves and deepens our connections with others.

When you allow yourself to be vulnerable, you tear down the walls that isolation builds and invite others into your world. This act of openness can transform relationships, fostering a deeper understanding and empathy between individuals. It can also enhance your self-awareness, as acknowledging and expressing your vulnerabilities requires a deep and honest self-reflection often avoided in daily interactions. Moreover, embracing vulnerability can lead to a significant reduction in the stress and anxiety associated with maintaining an "everything is fine" facade. The energy that once went into guarding against any perceived weaknesses can now be redirected toward more constructive, fulfilling endeavors.

However, embracing vulnerability is not about oversharing or seeking attention; it's about being honest about your feelings and experiences in a way that is appropriate and respectful to the context and the people involved. It requires discernment and sensitivity to others' boundaries, ensuring this openness leads to mutual understanding and respect.

Vulnerability and Connection

One of the most transformative aspects of vulnerability is its ability to forge deeper connections with others. When you share your fears, struggles, and uncertainties, you offer a gift of your inner world. This act can evoke empathy and compassion from others, who often can relate to such feelings from their own experiences. It creates a space for genuine interaction, where pretenses disappear, and authentic communication can flourish.

This authenticity is crucial in all relationships, whether personal or professional. In personal relationships, vulnerability fosters intimacy and trust, laying a foundation for more profound love and understanding. In professional contexts, it can humanize workplace interactions, breaking down hierarchical barriers and fostering a culture of open communication and mutual respect. Leaders who show vulnerability are often perceived as more approachable and relatable, qualities that can inspire loyalty and drive among their teams.

However, becoming vulnerable can feel like a high-stakes risk if you're used to keeping your guard up. It requires a shift from seeing emotional exposure as something that could lead to judgment or rejection to viewing it as an opportunity for deepening relationships and personal growth.

Barrier to Vulnerability

Despite its benefits, many barriers can inhibit the embrace of vulnerability. The most significant is fear of rejection or judgment. Many fear that showing their true selves will lead to being misunderstood, disliked, or ostracized. Cultural norms and personal upbringing can also play a significant role in discouraging vulnerability. Opening up can seem counterintuitive or even dangerous in societies or families where showing emotions is equated with weakness.

To overcome these hurdles, it's essential to start small. Begin by sharing minor vulnerabilities with trusted friends or family members who will likely respond with empathy and support. This practice can help build your confidence in vulnerability and help you realize that the anticipated adverse outcomes are often much worse in our imaginations than in reality.

Exercises to Practice Vulnerability

Practicing vulnerability can be facilitated through specific exercises designed to gradually increase your comfort with opening up. One effective exercise is the "Vulnerability Walk," where you share personal stories or feelings with a friend during a walk. The side-by-side nature of walking, as opposed to face-to-face interaction, can make it easier to share more freely, reducing the intensity of the exposure.

Another exercise is the "Three Levels of Why," which involves exploring the reasons behind your feelings or actions by asking "why" three times. For example, if you're upset about a friend canceling plans, ask yourself why this bothers you. Your first answer might be that it makes you feel unimportant. Ask why feeling unimportant bothers you. It may tap into deeper fears of loneliness or rejection. This exercise can deepen your self-understanding and help you communicate more clearly with others about your feelings.

Additionally, consider setting up a "Vulnerability Session" with close colleagues or friends where each person shares something personal about themselves. This structured approach can provide a safe space for everyone to practice vulnerability and help build group trust and cohesion.

By gradually integrating these practices into your life, you can begin dismantling the fears associated with vulnerability, replacing them with a strengthened capacity for connection, authenticity, and emotional resilience. Embracing vulnerability enriches your relationships and profoundly transforms your engagement with the world, opening up new avenues for growth and fulfillment.

Setting Achievable Goals: The SMART Framework

In the landscape of self-improvement, setting goals is akin to plotting a course on a map, providing direction and a means to measure progress. The SMART framework stands as a beacon in this process, offering a structured approach that enhances the likelihood of turning your aspirations into reality. SMART—an acronym for Specific, Measurable, Achievable, Relevant, and Time-bound—transforms vague ambitions into clear, actionable paths.

Introduction to the SMART Framework

The essence of the SMART framework is to infuse your goals with clarity and feasibility. An "I want to be more successful" goal is transformed under SMART criteria into "I aim to increase my sales by 15% in the next quarter by increasing client interactions to 10 per week and enhancing follow-up procedures." This refined goal now provides a clear direction and criteria for measuring success. Each element of SMART serves a unique purpose: Specific goals eliminate ambiguity and foster focus; Measurable aspects allow for tracking progress; Achievable ensures the goal is within reach, considering current resources and constraints; Relevant aligns the goal with broader life or career objectives, ensuring it's worthwhile; Time-bound assigns a deadline, creating urgency and prompting action.

Creating SMART Goals

Crafting SMART goals begins with a deep dive into what you truly want to achieve, dissecting it to fit each SMART criterion. Start by specifying your goal as clearly as possible. If your aim is career advancement, for example, determine what that looks like— perhaps securing a management position. Next, ensure measurability by defining success in tangible terms, such as obtaining a particular role within a year. Assess achievability by considering your current skills and the gaps you must fill to reach your goal. Relevance checks if this goal aligns with your long-term career aspirations. Finally, set a reasonable timeline to achieve your goal, keeping it ambitious yet realistic. This structured approach sets clear guidelines and primes you for the commitment needed to cross it.

Overcoming Obstacles to Achieving Goals

While setting SMART goals lays a solid foundation, encountering obstacles is inevitable. Common barriers include a lack of resources, external pressures, or unforeseen changes in circumstances. Overcoming these requires flexibility and resilience. One effective strategy is anticipating potential challenges during the planning phase and developing contingency plans. For instance, if your goal is to improve your education, potential obstacles might include financial constraints or time management issues. Planning might involve researching scholarship opportunities or adjusting your daily schedule to allocate study time. Maintaining a problem-solving mindset also helps navigate obstacles more fluidly, viewing them as puzzles to solve rather than impassable roadblocks.

Tracking and Adjusting Goals

The dynamic nature of life means that the path to your goals may need adjusting along the way. Regular tracking of your progress is crucial. Analyze weekly reviews of what was accomplished towards the goal and what wasn't, adjusting tactics accordingly. Monitoring progress helps maintain motivation, as each small success is a step closer to your ultimate goal. It also allows you to revise your approach in response to feedback or changing circumstances, ensuring that your strategies remain effective and aligned with your objectives.

As you integrate the SMART framework into your goal-setting practices, you infuse your aspirations with clarity and strategic foresight. This approach enhances the likelihood of achieving what you set out to do and aligns closely with the broader themes of personal growth discussed throughout this chapter. From cultivating a growth mindset to embracing resilience and the power of reflection, setting SMART goals is a practical application of these concepts, turning the theoretical into the tangible.

In wrapping up, remember that the personal development journey is continuous and ever-evolving. The strategies and insights discussed here are steps and tools for building a more intentional and fulfilling life. As we move into the next chapter, we'll explore how emotional well-being and mindfulness enrich this journey, offering more substantial insights into managing life's complexities with grace and resilience.

Emotional Well-being and Mindfulness

Imagine standing at the edge of a serene lake, the surface so calm it mirrors the sky above, undisturbed by even a ripple. This image of tranquility is a physical state and a metaphor for what mindfulness can bring to our minds. Amidst the turbulence of daily life, where stress often seems as natural as breathing, mindfulness offers a sanctuary of calm where we can restore balance and foster a deeper connection with ourselves. This chapter invites you to explore the gentle yet powerful practice of mindfulness, a tool not just for reducing stress but for enhancing overall emotional well-being.

Introduction to Mindfulness: Practices for Everyday Life

Defining Mindfulness

Mindfulness is the practice of being fully present and engaged at the moment, aware of your thoughts and feelings without distraction or judgment. It involves a conscious direction of our awareness away from the automatic pilot of day-to-day activities and into the current experience. This might sound simple, but it's a robust antidote to the stresses of modern lives, which often push us to dwell on past regrets or future anxieties. The benefits of mindfulness are supported by a growing body of research showing its positive impacts on various aspects of mental health, including stress reduction, emotion regulation, and increased resilience.

Simple Mindfulness Practices

Incorporating mindfulness into your daily life can be simple and does not necessarily require extensive time commitments. One basic technique is mindful breathing, where you focus solely on your breath, the inhale and exhale. You can do this for just a few minutes each day, and it serves as a mental reset button, clearing out cluttered thoughts and bringing you back to your center. Another practice is the body scan, where you mentally scan your body from head to toe, observing sensations without judgment. This can be particularly helpful for reconnecting with your physical self and calming your mind before sleep.

Mindfulness and Stress Reduction

The pace of modern life often leaves us in a chronic state of stress triggered by a relentless stream of demands and worries. Mindfulness cuts through this stress by bringing our attention back to the present. This shift in focus can significantly reduce our bodies' cortisol levels, the stress hormone. Regular mindfulness practice teaches us to respond to stressful situations more calmly and thoughtfully rather than reacting impulsively. Moreover, mindfulness helps us recognize when we start to spiral into stress-inducing thoughts or emotions, allowing us to steer back toward balance and peace more quickly.

Incorporating Mindfulness into the Routine

Making mindfulness a sustainable part of your daily routine can transform it from a practice into a way of living. Begin by integrating short sessions of mindfulness into your daily schedule. This could be a few minutes of mindful breathing each morning before you start your day or a brief body scan each night before you sleep. Another practical approach is to apply mindfulness to everyday activities like eating or walking. Eat one meal mindfully each day, focusing on your food's flavors, textures, and sensations. Or try a mindful walk, where you concentrate fully on the experience of walking, noticing the sensations in your feet and the air on your skin. These practices don't require extra time; they require a shift in your attention.

Mindfulness: A Path to Better Health and Stability

Mindfulness, rooted in ancient traditions but backed by modern science, offers a promising pathway to better health and increased emotional stability. By learning to anchor ourselves in the here and now, we cultivate a skill that can profoundly transform the quality of our lives. As we continue to explore the depths of emotional well-being and mindfulness, let these practices be your first step towards a more peaceful, centered life.

Managing Emotional Triggers: Strategies for Calm and Control

Emotions can surge through us with the force of a storm, turning a seemingly ordinary day into a whirlwind of reactions. Understanding what ignites these emotional responses—known as triggers—can often feel like detective work where you are both the investigator and the subject. Identifying your emotional triggers is the first step toward gaining control over them rather than allowing them to steer your reactions. Typically, these triggers are rooted in past experiences, deeply held beliefs or unresolved issues. For instance, if criticism is a significant trigger for you, it might be tied to an underlying fear of not being good enough, perhaps stemming from demanding expectations placed on you in childhood. By mapping these connections, you become more aware of why certain situations unsettle you and empower yourself to anticipate and manage your reactions more effectively.

Techniques for Managing Reactions

Once you've identified your triggers, the next step is to master techniques for managing your reactions. This is where practices like breathing exercises come into play. Breathing is our most fundamental connection to life, yet its power is often underestimated. The next time you find yourself triggered, try this: pause and take a deep, slow breath. Fill your lungs, and then release the breath slowly. This simple act can help deactivate the body's stress response and reengage the thinking part of your brain, the prefrontal cortex, which is essential for responding rather than reacting. Another powerful technique is cognitive reframing, which involves changing your perspective on the triggering event. For example, if someone's harsh words trigger you, reframe your interpretation: perhaps this person is under stress, and it's not about you. This shift in perspective can diffuse the emotional intensity, allowing for a more measured response.

Preventing Trigger Overwhelm

Preventing trigger overwhelm is necessary, especially in high-stress or emotionally charged situations. One effective strategy is setting clear personal boundaries, knowing what you can handle and when to step back. This might mean taking a five-minute break during a heated discussion or not engaging in particular topics in stressful settings. Additionally, regular activities that bolster your psychological resilience, such as yoga, meditation, or even hobbies like painting or writing, can provide a buffer against emotional overwhelm. These activities strengthen your mind's ability to cope with stress and enhance your self-awareness and emotional intelligence, making you less susceptible to being blindsided by your triggers.

Creating a Personalized Emotional Response Plan

Creating a personalized emotional response plan is a proactive way to handle triggers. Begin by listing out common triggers and the emotions they evoke. Next to each, outline a strategy that has worked in the past or a new one you wish to try, such as taking deep breaths, using positive affirmations, or discussing your feelings with a trusted friend. Keep this plan accessible—perhaps as a note in your phone or a journal entry—and review it regularly. By preparing responses in advance, you can feel more confident and in control when triggers arise, ensuring your emotions do not get the best of you. This personalized plan acts not just as a guide but as a reminder that you are in control and capable of navigating through emotional storms with grace and resilience.

Understanding and Directing Emotions

As you continue to explore and apply these strategies, you'll likely discover that managing emotional triggers is not about suppressing your feelings but understanding and directing them in a way that serves you. This process enhances your well-being and enriches your interactions with others, leading to more meaningful and harmonious relationships. By mastering the art of emotional management, you equip yourself with tools that transform potential conflicts into opportunities for growth and deeper understanding.

The Science of Happiness: Habits for Cultivating Joy

Happiness often feels like a fleeting, elusive state we chase, hoping to capture it permanently. Yet, what if the pursuit itself is structured to make happiness more of a natural byproduct rather than a distant goal? Positive psychology, which focuses on amplifying the good in life rather than merely mitigating the bad, provides a framework for cultivating practical and profound happiness. This approach shifts the focus from what's wrong to what's strong, from alleviating suffering to building and capitalizing on sources of joy and contentment in our daily lives.

The PERMA Model

One of the core principles of positive psychology is the PERMA model, developed by psychologist Martin Seligman, which outlines five essential elements of psychological well-being and happiness: Positive Emotions, Engagement, Relationships, Meaning, and Accomplishment. Each component contributes to the overall well-being, and understanding how to cultivate each aspect can significantly enhance your ability to experience joy. For instance, fostering positive emotions isn't just about feeling good but also recognizing and savoring these feelings when they occur. Techniques such as mindfulness and cognitive-behavioral strategies can help you amplify these moments of joy, making them more prevalent in your everyday life.

Daily Habits for Sustaining Happiness

Building on this foundation, daily habits are crucial in sustaining happiness. Consider the habit of journaling, which can be a powerful tool for engaging with your thoughts and feelings in a structured way. Writing down three things you are grateful for each day, for example, can shift your focus from what's lacking to what's abundant in your life, cultivating a mindset of abundance and appreciation. Similarly, setting aside time for activities that immerse you in a state of 'flow'—where you are so engaged in what you're doing that you lose track of time—can significantly boost your engagement and satisfaction with life. This could be anything from painting, writing, playing a musical instrument, or coding—whatever draws you in and makes the world disappear.

The Role of Gratitude and Positive Outlook

Gratitude and a positive outlook cannot be overstated in their impact on happiness. Gratitude, in particular, has been shown to strengthen relationships, improve physical health, enhance empathy, reduce aggression, and improve self-esteem. It acts as a buffer against negative emotions such as envy, resentment, and regret. You can improve your sense of well-being by simply acknowledging the good in your life and, more importantly, recognizing that the source of that good often lies outside yourself. Practices such as keeping a gratitude journal or sending thank-you notes can make expressions of gratitude more tangible and routine, further ingraining this positive habit in your life.

Overcoming Obstacles to Happiness

However, the path to happiness is often obstructed by various common obstacles. One is hedonic adaptation—the phenomenon where individuals return to a baseline level of happiness regardless of what happens in their lives, whether positive or negative. This can make sustained happiness seem unattainable. Overcoming this and other obstacles often requires a shift in mindset. For instance, instead of constantly seeking new pleasures or acquisitions in the hope of lasting happiness, focus on appreciating what you currently have and finding new ways to enjoy it. This could involve varying your routines, mixing social interactions, or changing your environment to keep your experiences fresh and engaging.

Adapting Your Lifestyle for Sustained Joy

Adapting your lifestyle to prioritize activities that promote these components of happiness is about adding more joy to your life and building resilience against life's inevitable adversities. By actively cultivating positive emotions, engaging deeply in your passions, nurturing fulfilling relationships, seeking meaning, and celebrating your accomplishments, you create a robust framework for a life not just lived but well-lived. As we continue to explore these themes, remember that each small habit, each moment of gratitude, and each positive interaction is a step towards a happier, more fulfilled you.

Building Emotional Resilience: The Key to Bouncing Back

Emotional resilience is often likened to a tree bending in a storm; it sways and flexes under the force of the wind, yet it does not break. In psychological terms, emotional resilience refers to one's ability to adapt to stress and adversity while maintaining psychological well-being. This capability is crucial because life invariably presents us with challenges and setbacks. Without resilience, these events can lead to significant emotional distress, potentially impacting our mental health and overall quality of life. Developing resilience equips you with the tools to face difficulties head-on, recover more quickly from setbacks, and emerge stronger than before.

Enhancing Resilience through Support Networks

Building this kind of resilience is not an innate trait but a cultivated skill, and several strategies can significantly enhance your capacity to bounce back. One of the foundational elements of resilience is developing a solid support network. This network can include family, friends, colleagues, or members of community groups who provide emotional support and practical help during tough times. These relationships offer a buffer against the effects of stress and provide a sounding board and perspective when you're too close to a problem to see the way forward. To strengthen your network, invest time nurturing these relationships, offering support to others, and being open to receiving help when needed.

The Role of Self-Care in Building Resilience

Another crucial strategy is the practice of self-care, which involves taking deliberate actions to care for your physical and emotional health. This might include regular exercise, which improves physical health and has considerable benefits for your mood and mental well-being due to the release of endorphins.

Adequate sleep and a nutritious diet are vital to good self-care, impacting cognitive function and emotional regulation. Engaging in activities you enjoy that give you a sense of accomplishment is equally essential. Whether reading, gardening, painting, or playing a musical instrument, these activities can provide a valuable outlet for stress relief and joy.

The Symbiotic Relationship between Resilience and Mental Health

The relationship between resilience and mental health is symbiotic. Enhanced resilience contributes to better mental health by reducing the risk of developing mental health disorders such as anxiety and depression, which are often triggered or exacerbated by unmanaged stress. Conversely, good mental health can bolster resilience by providing the psychological resources needed to cope with life's challenges. It's a cycle that promotes a more robust ability to navigate the complexities and hardships of life.

Real-Life Stories of Resilience

To illustrate the power of resilience, consider the stories of individuals who have demonstrated remarkable emotional resilience. One such person is a young woman who, after losing her job unexpectedly, used the setback to reevaluate her career goals. Instead of spiraling into despair, she focused on what she could control—her response to the situation. She began freelancing and taking online courses related to her field, slowly building a portfolio that eventually led to a better, more satisfying job opportunity. Her story highlights how resilience can transform a potentially devastating situation into a catalyst for personal growth and career redirection. Another compelling example comes from a man who overcame a severe illness that left him bedridden for months. He maintained a hopeful outlook throughout his recovery, setting small, manageable daily goals. Whether it was sitting up in bed for an hour or walking to the hallway, each little victory fueled his motivation to keep going. His resilience facilitated his physical recovery and inspired those around him. His journey underscores a resilient mindset's profound impact on the individual and the broader community.

Cultivating Resilience in Your Life

These stories, and countless others like them, serve as powerful reminders of the strength of the human spirit. They provide insight into the strategies that can foster resilience, offering hope and guidance to those facing their storms. As you reflect on these narratives and the principles discussed, consider how you might integrate these resilience-building practices into your life, bolstering your capacity to navigate future challenges with strength and grace.

The Art of Letting Go: Strategies for Releasing Emotional Baggage

Navigating through life, we often accumulate emotional baggage without fully realizing its weight until one day, the burden becomes palpable, influencing our actions, thoughts, and relationships. Emotional baggage, a term used to describe unresolved emotional issues from the past, can subtly dictate how we interact with others and perceive the world. Recognizing when past experiences and feelings dictate your current behavior can be transformative. For example, if you react intensely to situations that others seem to handle easily or if specific interactions consistently trigger feelings of sadness or anger, it may indicate underlying emotional baggage. This recognition is crucial as it marks the first step towards healing and growth.

Techniques for Letting Go

Letting go of emotional baggage is neither straightforward nor easy, but it's profoundly liberating. Techniques such as forgiveness exercises can be particularly effective. In this context, forgiveness isn't about excusing the actions that hurt you but about freeing yourself from the hold they have on your emotional well-being. This might involve writing a letter of forgiveness to the person who hurt you (which you don't have to send) or simply deciding internally to release the resentment and pain associated with that memory. Cognitive-behavioral strategies also play a significant role in this process. These strategies involve recognizing and restructuring negative thought patterns contributing to your emotional burden. For instance, replacing thoughts that revolve around victimhood or blame with thoughts that focus on recovery and empowerment can significantly alter your emotional landscape, paving the way for healing.

Seeking Professional Help

There are times, however, when the weight of emotional baggage feels too heavy to lift on your own, and this is when professional help can be invaluable. Engaging with a therapist or counselor provides a supportive space to explore deeply ingrained emotional issues. These professionals can help you navigate your feelings more effectively, offering tools and strategies tailored to your needs. Therapy can be particularly beneficial for those dealing with long-standing issues like trauma or chronic anxiety, providing a framework for understanding and overcoming these challenges.

Creating Space for New Experiences

Letting go creates space for new experiences and relationships. It's like clearing out weeds in a garden to allow new flowers to bloom. Without the old resentments and pains hogging your emotional space, you open up to new possibilities. Engaging in new activities, forming new relationships, or revisiting old relationships with a fresh perspective can all be part of this new chapter. The energy once spent on nursing old wounds can now fuel new adventures and connections, enriching your life in ways previously overshadowed by your emotional baggage.

Embracing Freedom and New Beginnings

As this chapter of emotional unburdening closes, remember the freedom that comes with letting go. You've explored recognizing the signs of emotional baggage, learned effective techniques for release, understood when to seek professional help, and envisioned the new joys that await on the other side of letting go. Each step, though challenging, is a stride towards a lighter, more fulfilled existence.

Transition to Interpersonal Relationships

Transitioning from the personal themes of emotional well-being and mindfulness, the next chapter will delve into the obstructions that keep us stuck. Here, we'll explore how our newfound insights into personal emotional health can enhance and transform our interactions with obstacles, leading to profound, more fulfilling results.

Overcoming Obstacles to Change

Imagine standing at the foot of a towering mountain, its peak obscured by clouds. You know the climb will be arduous, filled with unseen obstacles and unexpected challenges. Yet, the promise of the view from the summit propels you forward. This mountain is a metaphor for the personal changes we strive to achieve—the ascent represents the journey of transformation, fraught with hurdles that often manifest as self-sabotage. This section delves into understanding and overcoming this self-imposed barrier, transforming it from an impediment to a stepping stone toward self-improvement.

Identifying and Overcoming Self-Sabotage

Recognizing Self-Sabotage

Self-sabotage is an intriguing paradox where the very behaviors meant to safeguard us from failure become the architects of our setbacks. It's the diet forgotten with a slice of cake, the snoozed alarm that leads to a missed workout, or the procrastination on a project until it becomes a source of panic. Recognizing these patterns is the first step toward change. You might notice self-sabotage in habits that consistently hinder your progress or a recurrent reluctance to embrace new opportunities that align with your goals. The key lies in vigilant self-observation—monitoring your actions and the accompanying emotions. This awareness can illuminate behaviors that subvert your success.

For instance, you might find that you repeatedly miss deadlines or fail to follow through on commitments despite your best intentions. This can manifest as consistently arriving late to important meetings, avoiding tasks you know will advance your career, or engaging in behaviors that undermine your health goals, such as eating junk food or skipping exercise. These actions, often driven by subconscious fears or insecurities, create a cycle of self-defeat that can be challenging to break. By paying close attention to the moments when you sabotage your efforts, you can begin to understand the triggers and motivations behind these behaviors.

Understanding the Reasons Behind Self-Sabotage

At its core, self-sabotage is often rooted in fear of failure, the unknown, or success. Psychological theories suggest that such behaviors serve as a protective mechanism, shielding one from potential disappointment or the anxiety of stepping out of a comfort zone. For instance, fear of failure may lead you to postpone preparing for an important presentation under the guise of needing to find the perfect starting point. Another profound contributor to self-sabotage is imposter syndrome, where, despite external achievements, an internal narrative convinces you that you are not worthy and that any success is due to luck. This can undermine your efforts to align your reality with your belief of being a 'fraud.'

Self-sabotage can also stem from deep-seated beliefs formed during childhood or past experiences. These beliefs might include thoughts like "I'm not good enough," "I don't deserve success," or "If I try, I might fail." These limiting beliefs can drive self-sabotaging behaviors to avoid confronting these uncomfortable feelings. Additionally, self-sabotage can be linked to a fear of success. While it might seem counterintuitive, the prospect of achieving your goals can be intimidating. Success often brings increased expectations and responsibilities, and the fear of not being able to maintain this new level of achievement can lead to behaviors that prevent success from happening in the first place.

Strategies to Overcome Self-Sabotage

Counteracting self-sabotage requires a blend of strategic planning and emotional recalibration. Begin by setting clear, achievable goals. Break larger goals into smaller, manageable tasks to avoid the overwhelm that often triggers self-sabotage. For example, instead of aiming to write a book in a month, set a daily goal to write a page or a chapter. This approach makes the task seem less daunting and more achievable, reducing the likelihood of procrastination and other self-defeating behaviors.

Complement this strategy with the practice of self-compassion—be kind to yourself when setbacks occur. Understand that perfection is an illusion and that mistakes are part of growth.

Engage in positive self-talk and reframe failures as lessons learned, not catastrophes. For example, if you miss a workout, instead of criticizing yourself, acknowledge the slip-up and focus on getting back on track the next day. This shift in perspective can help reduce the negative emotions associated with self-sabotage and encourage a more proactive and resilient mindset.

Another effective strategy is to identify and challenge the limiting beliefs that fuel self-sabotage. This can be done through cognitive-behavioral techniques, such as cognitive restructuring, which involves identifying and replacing irrational thoughts with more balanced, constructive ones. For example, if you catch yourself thinking: "I'll never be able to complete this project," challenge that thought by reminding yourself of past successes and the skills you possess that will help you succeed. By systematically confronting these negative thoughts, you can weaken their power and reduce the impulse to engage in self-defeating behaviors.

Transforming Self-Sabotage into Self-Improvement

Transforming self-sabotage into a tool for self-improvement involves changing how you interpret and react to your actions. You can dissect each act of self-sabotage to uncover the underlying fears or beliefs driving it. Regular reflection can be facilitated through journaling, providing insights into patterns and triggers of self-sabotage. Write about instances when you've sabotaged yourself: what were you trying to avoid? What would have been the worst outcome of taking action? Often, you'll find that the risk of action is less daunting than the paralysis of inaction.

Consider cognitive-behavioral techniques that challenge and reframe irrational fears and beliefs to aid in this transformative process. Techniques such as cognitive restructuring can help alter the negative thought patterns that fuel self-sabotage. By systematically confronting these thoughts and replacing them with more balanced, constructive ones, you can reduce the impulse to engage in self-defeating behaviors.

This exploration of self-sabotage illuminates the shadows where our fears hide and offers a lantern for navigating through them. By understanding and addressing the roots of self-sabotage, you reclaim your power to direct the course of your change, turning obstacles into opportunities for personal growth and self-discovery. As you continue to engage with these strategies, remember that the journey of change is not about reaching a destination but about evolving along the way, continuously adapting, and growing.

Seeking Support and Professional Guidance

Overcoming self-sabotage can be challenging, and seeking support from others can be incredibly beneficial. Sharing your experiences with friends, family, or a support group can give you different perspectives and encouragement. Sometimes, an external viewpoint can help you see patterns and solutions you might have missed. Additionally, consider seeking professional help from a therapist or counselor, particularly if your self-sabotage behaviors are deeply entrenched or linked to past trauma. A professional can help you explore these issues in depth and provide targeted strategies to overcome them.

Therapists can use various approaches, such as cognitive-behavioral therapy (CBT), to help you identify and change the thought patterns and behaviors contributing to self-sabotage. They can also provide a safe space to explore your fears and anxieties and develop healthier coping mechanisms. Coaching is another option, particularly for those looking to achieve specific goals. A coach can help you set realistic objectives, develop actionable plans, and hold you accountable, ensuring that you stay on track and overcome the tendency to self-sabotage.

Building Resilience and Maintaining Progress

Building resilience is crucial for maintaining progress as you work towards overcoming self-sabotage. Resilience involves developing the ability to bounce back from setbacks and continue pursuing your goals despite challenges. Practicing mindfulness and stress management techniques, such as meditation, yoga, or deep-breathing exercises, can help you stay grounded and focused, reducing the likelihood of falling back into self-sabotaging behaviors.

Additionally, celebrate your successes, no matter how small. Acknowledging and rewarding your progress can boost your motivation and reinforce positive behaviors. Keep track of your achievements and reflect on how far you've come, which can provide a sense of accomplishment and encourage you to keep moving forward. Remember that overcoming self-sabotage is a journey, and setbacks are a natural part of the process. View them as opportunities to learn and grow rather than failures when they occur.

By integrating these strategies into your daily life, you can gradually dismantle the patterns of self-sabotage and replace them with behaviors that support your success and well-being. As you continue on this path, you will find that you are more capable and resilient than you may have believed, equipped with the tools and insights to create a fulfilling and successful life.

Dealing with Setbacks: A Guide to Getting Back on Track

Setbacks are as much a part of life as breathing; they are inevitable, regardless of who you are or what goals you pursue. Often, these setbacks are perceived negatively as detours on the road to success. However, when viewed through a lens of growth and learning, they become invaluable experiences, enriching our journey with wisdom and resilience. Normalizing the occurrence of setbacks is crucial—it removes the stigma of failure and reframes these moments as natural, expected steps in achieving any significant outcome. Whether it's a rejected project proposal, an unachieved personal goal, or an unexpected life event, setbacks are not roadblocks but stepping stones that provide profound opportunities for personal development and insight.

The initial reaction might be disappointment or frustration when faced with a setback. However, the key to turning these situations into opportunities for growth lies in a structured assessment of what happened. Start by distancing yourself emotionally from the situation to gain a clear, objective view. Ask yourself what the expectation was and what the outcome was. What were the contributing factors that led to this result? Considering internal actions and external circumstances, this analysis should be as detailed as possible. For instance, if a job promotion still needs to be achieved, consider your preparedness, the quality of your work, the criteria used for promotion, and perhaps even the economic climate of the industry. Each of these elements provides clues on what can be improved or adjusted. Learning from setbacks involves extracting actionable insights from each situation, which can be applied to future endeavors, increasing your chances of success.

Creating a plan to bounce back from setbacks involves outlining specific steps based on the insights gained from your assessment. This plan should include short-term recovery actions and long-term adjustments to prevent the recurrence of the same setbacks. For example, if the setback was due to a lack of necessary skills, the immediate plan might include enrolling in relevant training or workshops. A long-term strategy could involve a mentorship arrangement to continuously develop and refine these skills. Each step in your plan should be actionable, measurable, and time-bound, ensuring that it addresses the immediate aftermath of the setback and strategically positions you for future success. Scheduling regular progress reviews can also be beneficial, allowing for adjustments to the plan as you gather more feedback and learn from ongoing experiences.

The role of resilience in managing and overcoming setbacks cannot be overstated. Resilience is not just about bouncing back to your original form, like a spring returning to its shape after being stretched; it's about adapting and finding new ways to move forward. Cultivating resilience involves developing a mindset that views challenges as catalysts for growth. It encompasses maintaining a positive outlook, managing emotions effectively, and pursuing your goals despite difficulties. Building resilience can be fostered by maintaining good physical health, nurturing positive relationships, and practicing mindfulness and stress-reduction techniques. These practices enhance your well-being, providing a solid foundation for tackling challenges. Additionally, resilience is reinforced by experiences—every setback overcome adds a layer of confidence and a toolkit of strategies that enhance your ability to handle future challenges.

In embracing these strategies for dealing with setbacks, you equip yourself with the tools to get back on track and the mindset to navigate future challenges more effectively. This approach repairs paths and builds new roads, each setback providing the knowledge and insight to pave the way forward. As you continue to apply these principles, remember that setbacks are not reflections of your capabilities but opportunities for growth and learning. Each challenge faced and overcome is a testament to your resilience and a step towards increased success and fulfillment.

Navigating Life Transitions: Strategies for Adaptation and Growth

Life transitions, whether expected, like graduating from college, starting a new job, moving to a new city, or unexpected, such as a sudden illness or losing a loved one, are inherent parts of our existence. These periods of change can significantly disrupt your sense of stability and can be a source of stress and anxiety. However, they also present unique opportunities for personal growth and self-discovery. Recognizing these transitions as they occur is crucial. It might be helpful to think of life transitions as any event or series of events that result in significant changes in the fabric of your daily life or outlook. Awareness of these shifts allows you to approach them with intention and mindfulness.

The first step in effectively managing life transitions is to embrace change as an opportunity. This mindset shift is pivotal. Instead of viewing change as a threat to your stability, see it as a chance to expand your horizons and learn something new about yourself and the world. For instance, starting a new job is not just a new set of responsibilities; it's an opportunity to acquire new skills, meet new people, and improve your career path. This perspective encourages openness and curiosity, which are essential for navigating transitions with resilience and adaptability.

You can employ several strategies to navigate these transitions effectively. Flexibility is key. Life rarely unfolds in a linear fashion, and being too rigid in your expectations or plans can lead to frustration and disappointment. Cultivate flexibility by setting goals with room for adjustment and being open to new experiences that may not align perfectly with your initial plans. For example, if a career move to another city doesn't turn out as planned, being open to exploring new industries or roles instead of clinging to the original plan can lead to unexpected and fulfilling career developments.

Seeking support during transitions is also essential. This can come from friends, family, professional mentors, or support groups. People who have undergone similar changes can provide empathy, practical advice, and invaluable insights during such times. They can act as sounding boards and provide reassurance that you are not alone in experiencing the challenges and joys that come with significant life changes.

In addition to these strategies, maintaining a positive outlook is essential. This doesn't mean ignoring the difficulties transitions can bring but approaching them with a mindset emphasizing growth and possibility. Celebrate small victories during times of change; these can significantly boost your morale. For instance, if you're adapting to life in a new city, celebrate milestones like making your first local friend or discovering a favorite new coffee shop. These experiences contribute to a sense of accomplishment and belonging, reinforcing a positive outlook.

The growth from navigating life transitions often manifests in ways that might not be immediately apparent. Over time, you may find that you have become more resilient, that your problem-solving skills have improved, or that you have developed a better understanding of what you truly value in life. For example, people who embrace the challenges of moving to a new country often talk about how the experience has broadened their perspectives, made them more adaptable, and opened up opportunities they had never considered.

Real-world stories abound of individuals finding remarkable personal growth through life transitions. Consider the story of a woman who turned a career-ending injury into an opportunity to pursue her passion for art, eventually becoming a celebrated painter. Or think of someone who, after a difficult divorce, used the transition to rediscover personal interests and independence, leading to a more fulfilling and balanced life. These stories highlight the transformative potential of life transitions, showcasing how periods of change, while often challenging, can lead to significant personal evolution and new paths that enrich your life in ways you might not have imagined.

As you face your life transitions, remember that each change brings a landscape rich with potential for growth and discovery. With flexibility, support, and a positive outlook, you can navigate these changes with resilience and a proactive enthusiasm that turns each transition into a stepping stone toward a more prosperous, more fulfilling life.

The Impact of Social Relationships on Personal Change

Social relationships are pivotal in shaping our behaviors, influencing our decisions, and supporting our goals for personal change. The people you surround yourself with can propel you forward or hold you back. They can be sources of inspiration and motivation or reservoirs of negativity and doubt. Understanding how these dynamics work is crucial in leveraging your social circles to support the positive changes you wish to enact.

One of the most significant ways social relationships influence behavior change is through the mechanisms of support and accountability. When you share your goals and aspirations with friends, family, or colleagues, you open up a network of potential cheerleaders and accountability partners. For instance, having a workout buddy can significantly enhance your commitment if your goal is to improve your physical health. They not only join you in your activity but also help you stay on track on days when motivation wanes. This social support can be incredibly motivating, turning the often arduous task of personal change into a shared, enjoyable journey.

However, the influence of social relationships can sometimes be positive. Sometimes, the people around you might consciously or unconsciously sabotage your efforts. This can stem from their fears, insecurities, or resistance to change. Identifying these negative influences early and understanding the dynamics at play is essential.

For example, a friend might discourage you from pursuing further education out of fear that your advancing career might create distance between you. Recognizing these patterns allows you to address them constructively by having open conversations about your mutual worries and aspirations, transforming potential obstacles into opportunities to deepen mutual understanding and support.

Cultivating Supportive Relationships

Building and maintaining relationships that support your personal growth involves more than just surrounding yourself with positive people. It requires nurturing these relationships and engaging with them in ways that promote mutual growth and understanding. Start by being clear about your goals and the support you need. Communicate openly with your friends and family about your aspirations and the challenges you are facing. This keeps you accountable and allows them to understand better how they can support you.

Additionally, be proactive in supporting their goals. Relationships are a two-way street, and showing genuine interest and support for the ambitions of those around you can foster a culture of mutual encouragement and help. This might involve celebrating their successes, offering assistance when they face setbacks, or simply listening to them discuss their challenges. Such interactions strengthen bonds and create a supportive network that thrives on the success of all its members.

Setting Boundaries with Negative Influences

While it's vital to cultivate supportive relationships, it's equally crucial to set boundaries with people or groups that hinder your progress. This involves first identifying who or what these negative influences are. They could be individuals who consistently discourage you, habits that tie you to unproductive routines, or social settings that lead you away from your goals. Once identified, setting boundaries can be challenging but necessary. This might mean spending less time with certain people, changing how you interact in specific settings, or even ending relationships that are profoundly detrimental to your well-being.

Setting boundaries is not about creating conflict but protecting your space and respecting your needs. It allows you to control what influences you let into your life, ensuring that they align with your goals and values. Communicate your boundaries clearly and assertively, without apology. Most importantly, enforce them consistently. This might be uncomfortable initially, but it is essential for your growth and well-being.

Leveraging Social Networks for Success

In today's digital age, social networks extend beyond our immediate physical interactions. Online platforms offer vast opportunities for finding support, inspiration, and information. They can connect you with like-minded individuals, support groups, or mentors who can play a pivotal role in your journey of personal change. For example, joining online forums or social media groups focused on specific interests like entrepreneurship, health, or personal development can provide valuable resources, advice, and encouragement.

However, it's necessary to engage with these networks mindfully. Ensure that your online interactions remain positive and constructive. Be selective about the groups you join and the discussions you participate in. Aim to contribute positively, sharing your experiences and learning from others. This proactive engagement can turn your social networks into powerful motivation, accountability, and success tools.

Incorporating these strategies into your social interactions can transform your relationships into pillars of support for your change. By nurturing supportive relationships, setting clear boundaries, and effectively leveraging your immediate and extended social networks, you empower yourself to navigate the complexities of personal transformation with confidence and support.

Creating a Supportive Environment for Change

The spaces we inhabit, both physical and social, play a pivotal role in shaping our behaviors and influencing our ability to enact and sustain change. Consider how a cluttered desk might impact your productivity or how a supportive friend can encourage you to maintain a new fitness regimen. These are not mere coincidences but reflections of a fundamental truth: our environment significantly affects our ability to achieve and sustain change. Creating an environment that supports and reinforces the changes you wish to see in your life is imperative to foster personal growth.

The Role of Environment in Sustaining Change

The surrounding environment can be both a catalyst and a barrier to change. A well-organized, thoughtfully arranged space can inspire action and facilitate new habits. Conversely, a chaotic or unsupportive environment can undermine your efforts and sap your motivation. The physical environment includes your home, workplace, and other spaces where you spend significant time. Each should be arranged to support your goals. For instance, if you aim to eat healthier, your kitchen should support this goal by readily offering healthy foods and displaying motivational quotes about healthy living. Similarly, if your goal is to study more effectively, your study area should be free of distractions, well-lit, and equipped with all the necessary materials.

The social environment is equally influential. This encompasses the people you interact with regularly, including family, friends, colleagues, and even casual acquaintances. These individuals' attitudes, behaviors, and values can significantly impact their motivation and ability to persist with changes. Surrounding yourself with a supportive social circle that encourages and reinforces your efforts can make the difference between success and failure in achieving your goals. This doesn't mean you need to sever ties with anyone who doesn't fit this criterion, but it does mean spending more time with those who uplift you and perhaps less with those who drain your energy or deter your progress.

Practical Tips for Environment Optimization

Optimizing your environment to support change involves several practical steps. Start by conducting an audit of your physical spaces. Examine your home, workplace, or any other environment where you spend much time. Look for ways these spaces could be better organized to support your goals. If you're trying to break a habit of watching too much television, rearrange your living area to focus more on reading or other hobbies—perhaps by positioning a bookshelf next to your favorite chair and moving the TV to a less central location.

To optimize your social environment, evaluate your current relationships. Identify which supports your growth and which might hold you back. Seek out and nurture relationships with individuals who share your aspirations or have achieved goals similar to yours. These connections can provide valuable insight, encouragement, and a sense of a shared journey that can make sticking to your changes more manageable and enjoyable.

Incorporating Visual Reminders and Cues

Visual reminders and cues are dynamic tools for supporting habit formation and goal achievement. They are constant, subtle prompts to keep your goals top-of-mind and can significantly enhance your motivation. For example, placing a vision board in a prominent place in your home or office can continuously remind you of your aspirations. This board might display images representing your goals, such as pictures of places you want to travel to, symbols of health and fitness, or quotes from inspiring individuals.

You can also use more direct cues related to specific habits you're trying to develop. If you're working on meditating daily, setting up a dedicated meditation space with visible cues like a meditation cushion, calming artwork, or a timer can help cement this new habit. Each visual element is a reminder and an invitation to engage in the behavior you're trying to habitualize.

Community and Belonging

Finding or creating a community with similar values and goals can profoundly affect your ability to sustain change. Community provides a sense of belonging and an additional layer of support and accountability that can be incredibly motivating. Look for local or online groups that align with your interests—a fitness class, a book club, or a professional organization. Participating in community events and activities can reinforce your commitment to your goals and provide a network of like-minded individuals who can offer support, advice, and encouragement.

Engaging actively within these communities can also amplify your sense of accountability. Sharing your goals with the group and regularly updating them on your progress can increase your understanding of the obligation to follow through, not just for yourself but for your peers who are rooting for your success. This communal support creates a dynamic where everyone is invested in each other's success, fostering a positive, motivational environment that celebrates each milestone and provides support through each challenge.

Creating a supportive environment is about more than aesthetics or social fun; it is about constructing a physical and social space that echoes your aspirations, fortifies your motivation, and sustains your journey toward lasting change. By carefully curating your surroundings to align with your goals, you set the stage for temporary success and enduring transformation.

The Long-Term View: Sustaining Change Over Time

Maintaining the momentum of personal change over the long haul often presents a challenge as daunting as initiating the change itself. As time progresses, the initial burst of enthusiasm can wane, and the daily grind can make even the most passionate commitments feel like burdens. To sustain change, maintaining motivation is crucial. It requires a dynamic approach that includes revisiting and periodically adjusting your goals to reflect your growing insights and changing circumstances. Life is not static, and your goals shouldn't be either. For example, if you initially set a goal to run a marathon but enjoy cycling more over time, adjust your goal to complete a long-distance cycling event instead. This flexibility keeps your goals relevant and aligned with your passions, which is integral to maintaining motivation.

Routine and consistency also play pivotal roles in embedding new behaviors into your daily life. They transform what might initially feel foreign into second nature. Establish routines that anchor your new behaviors, making them integral parts of your day. For instance, if you want to write more, establish a routine where you write for an hour every morning before checking emails or social media. This ensures that you dedicate time to your writing and puts you in a productive mindset for the rest of the day. Consistency in this routine reinforces the behavior, making it a staple of your daily activities rather than something you need to find extra time for.

However, even the best-planned routines and goals can encounter plateaus—periods where progress seems to stall. Overcoming these plateaus requires a mix of persistence and innovation. Sometimes, pushing through requires you to double down on your efforts, perhaps by increasing the intensity of your activities or the time you dedicate to them. Other times, innovation is required; changing your approach can provide a new angle of attack against the staleness that often accompanies plateaus. If you're facing a plateau in weight loss, for example, trying a new type of workout or adjusting your diet can kickstart progress again.

Celebrating progress, no matter how small, and reflecting on your growth journey are essential practices that reinforce the value of your sustained efforts. Regularly take stock of where you started and where you are now. This boosts your morale and provides tangible proof of your capabilities. Celebrate these achievements; whether it's treating yourself to a nice dinner for reaching a milestone or simply taking a moment to acknowledge your progress, recognition is a powerful motivator. Moreover, reflection allows you to appreciate the journey, not just the destination. It provides insights into what works, what doesn't, and how you can continue to grow and adapt as you move forward.

Sustaining change over time is not just about sticking to a routine or mindlessly pushing toward a goal. It's about adapting to life's inevitable shifts, finding joy and value in the small victories, and consistently aligning your actions with the evolving vision of who you want to become. As you close this chapter and reflect on the strategies discussed, remember that each day brings new opportunities for growth and renewal. The next chapter will build on these ideas, exploring advanced strategies for personal and professional success, ensuring that the journey of self-improvement continues to evolve and expand, just like you.

Advanced Strategies for Personal and Professional Success

Imagine you are navigating a vast ocean, where each wave represents a growth potential, and every wind shift hints at new opportunities and challenges. In this expansive sea of professional and personal development, mentorship emerges as a beacon, guiding you through complex waters and offering both a map and a compass for your journey. This chapter will explore the profound impact of mentorship, a relationship that accelerates your growth and deepens your understanding of yourself and your aspirations. Through mentorship, you access wisdom that transcends your experiences, providing a unique blend of support, insight, and challenge to propel you toward your goals.

The Role of Mentorship in Personal Growth: Finding and Being a Mentor

The Benefits of Mentorship

At its core, mentorship is a symbiotic relationship that benefits both mentor and mentee, engaging in a dance of knowledge exchange and mutual growth. For the ones being mentored, the advantages are multifaceted. It offers a tailored learning experience that addresses personal and professional challenges, providing actionable advice often absent in books or formal education systems. Mentors can help identify opportunities and provide insights into navigating your career path, frequently accelerating your learning curve and helping you avoid common pitfalls. Moreover, mentors can be invaluable in expanding your professional network, introducing you to contacts that might otherwise be inaccessible.

The benefits are equally rewarding for mentors. Mentorship allows you to refine your leadership and communication skills, as teaching often clarifies your understanding and solidifies your knowledge. It provides a profound sense of fulfillment from contributing to someone else's growth and success. Furthermore, mentors usually gain fresh perspectives and new ideas from their mentees, keeping them connected to the latest trends and innovations within their field, which can invigorate their professional pursuits.

Finding the Right Mentor

Securing a mentor who can significantly impact your growth involves more than selecting an expert in your field. It requires finding someone whose experience aligns with your career aspirations and whose mentoring style complements your learning preferences. Start by identifying what you need guidance on— technical skills, industry insights, or career management. Professional associations, alumni networks, and LinkedIn are excellent resources for locating potential mentors. When reaching out, be clear about what you seek from the mentorship and what you bring. A well-defined proposal can distinguish between a polite decline and an enthusiastic acceptance.

Being an Effective Mentor

Effective mentorship is characterized by more than just imparting wisdom; it fosters a supportive environment where mentees can explore ideas, make mistakes, and grow. As a mentor, your role is to listen actively, offer constructive feedback, and challenge your mentees to stretch beyond their comfort zones. It's crucial to set clear expectations from the outset and establish open lines of communication. Regular meetings, whether virtual or face-to-face, help maintain the momentum of the relationship. Additionally, being sensitive to the mentee's feedback about the mentorship process and making necessary adjustments can enhance your guidance's effectiveness.

Maximizing the Mentor-Mentee Relationship

To maximize the benefits of a mentor-mentee relationship, it's essential to establish clear goals and revisit them periodically. This helps maintain focus and ensures the mentorship provides value aligned with the mentee's evolving needs. Encourage mutual respect and openness, where both parties feel comfortable sharing insights, asking questions, and expressing concerns. This dynamic fosters a fruitful learning environment and strengthens the mentor-mentee bond.

A successful mentorship relationship often evolves into a lifelong professional network and friendship, offering both parties sustained personal and professional growth. It is a testament to the power of collaborative development and the profound impact of sharing knowledge and experience.

In this ocean of continuous growth and learning, mentorship is not just a guiding star but a dynamic lighthouse. It illuminates your path with the wisdom of experienced navigators and enriches your journey with deep, personal interactions. As you continue to explore the expansive waters of your professional and personal development, remember that the relationships you build through mentorship can significantly shape your trajectory, offering guidance and a shared journey toward success.

Advanced Goal-Setting Techniques: Beyond the Basics

In personal and professional development, setting goals is akin to plotting a course on a map; it defines the destination and the path to get there. However, the terrain of life is ever-changing; thus, goal-setting must also be dynamic and adaptable. Traditional goal-setting focuses on static targets, but advanced techniques emphasize flexibility, allowing goals to evolve as your circumstances and growth dictate. This approach acknowledges that your aspirations might shift as you learn and grow, and your goals need to reflect these changes to remain relevant and motivating.

Setting Dynamic Goals

Dynamic goal-setting involves establishing clear and measurable goals and being flexible and responsive to changes in your environment or personal circumstances. This method encourages regular reassessment of your goals to ensure they align with your current needs and aspirations. For instance, if you set a goal to become a manager within your company but discover a passion for entrepreneurship over time, your goals must shift to reflect this new path. Dynamic goal-setting is not about changing your destination every time you face a challenge but rather about refining your trajectory based on enhanced self-awareness and changing external conditions. It requires a mindset open to growth and adaptability to new information, which can sometimes mean redefining what success looks like.

To implement dynamic goal-setting effectively, start by defining broad, long-term objectives and then break these down into smaller, more flexible goals. These smaller goals should be designed with the ability to pivot in mind, allowing you to adjust them without losing sight of your overall direction. Regularly scheduled reviews—monthly or quarterly—can facilitate this flexibility. During these reviews, assess the progress and relevance of your goals, making adjustments that reflect your latest insights and circumstances. This practice keeps your goals relevant and keeps you engaged and motivated, as it aligns your actions with your most current definitions of success.

Integrating Short-Term and Long-Term Goals

Integrating short-term and long-term goals creates a scaffold that supports sustained progress toward your overarching ambitions. Short-term goals act as milestones or checkpoints that lead to long-term objectives, providing opportunities for celebration and reassessment. This integration ensures that daily activities are connected to bigger aspirations, making the daily grind more meaningful and aligned with your ultimate objectives.

For effective integration, each long-term goal should be dissected into a series of short-term goals that are actionable and measurable. For example, if your long-term goal is to write a book, your short-term goals include completing an outline, writing a certain number of words daily, or securing a literary agent. Each of these contributes to the broader objective but is actionable. This breakdown makes the long-term goal more manageable and provides clear direction for daily activities, ensuring that every day contributes to your broader vision.

Visualization and Affirmation Techniques

Visualization and affirmation are powerful techniques that can reinforce your commitment to your goals and enhance your belief in your ability to achieve them. Visualization involves creating a mental image of attaining your goals, imagining the success and the steps taken to get there. This technique enhances motivation and clarifies the path to success. Affirmations, on the other hand, involve positive, proactive statements that reinforce your capability and commitment. Statements like "I am capable of leading projects successfully" or "I am a committed and prolific writer" help to cement a positive self-image and a can-do attitude.

Incorporating these techniques into your daily routine can significantly impact your mindset and behavior. Spend a few minutes each morning visualizing your success and reciting your affirmations. This practice sets a positive tone for the day, aligning your mental and emotional state with your goals and enhancing your confidence to take the necessary actions to achieve them.

Evaluating and Adjusting Goals

Regular evaluation of your goals is crucial in maintaining their relevance and effectiveness. This evaluation should examine the goals and strategies for achieving them. Ask yourself if the goals are still aligned with your personal and professional aspirations and if your methods for achieving them are effective. Are there new skills, resources, or changes in your environment that could necessitate a different approach? Could adjustments make your journey toward these goals more efficient or enjoyable?

Adjusting your goals might seem like a setback, but it is a proactive strategy that ensures your efforts are concentrated on what is most beneficial for your growth. It reflects an agile mindset, capable of responding to feedback and changing circumstances, qualities that are invaluable in today's fast-paced world. This adaptability keeps you moving forward and deepens your engagement with your personal and professional development, making the process as rewarding as the outcomes.

As you continue to refine your goal-setting techniques, remember that the ultimate aim is to foster an ongoing, dynamic relationship with your aspirations, one that continually inspires, challenges, and grows with you. This approach enhances your immediate achievements and ensures your journey is fulfilling, well-directed, and responsive to your evolving life narrative.

The Power of Networking: Building Relationships for Success

In today's interconnected world, the adage "It's not what you know, but who you know" has never been more pertinent. Networking is essential for anyone aiming to advance their career and enrich their personal growth. It's about creating a web of connections that can offer support, provide insights, and open doors to opportunities that might otherwise remain inaccessible. Networking goes beyond mere socializing; it involves strategic relationship-building with individuals who share similar professional interests or can challenge you to expand your horizons.

The importance of networking must be balanced, particularly in competitive job markets and industries where opportunities are often hidden or require a personal introduction to access. By connecting with others in your field, you gain visibility and tap into a reservoir of knowledge and experience that can propel your career forward. These connections can inspire, challenge your thinking, and provide critical feedback to enhance your professional development. Moreover, your network can offer guidance and support in career transition or uncertainty, helping you navigate challenges more effectively.

Strategies for Effective Networking

Effective networking is both an art and a science. It begins with a clear understanding of your goals: Are you seeking a new job, looking for business partners, or simply aiming to stay informed about industry trends? Once your goals are defined, identify networking events, professional groups, conferences, and social gatherings where you can meet like-minded individuals. When attending these events, approach conversations with genuine curiosity. Ask insightful questions that reveal a deeper understanding of the person's expertise and show your interest in their experiences and opinions. This approach makes the interaction more engaging and leaves a memorable impression, increasing the likelihood of a lasting professional relationship.

Following up is crucial in networking. After meeting someone, send a personalized message referencing specific topics discussed during your conversation. This could be through email, a LinkedIn message, or even a phone call. Express your appreciation for the knowledge shared and your interest in staying connected. Suggest a follow-up meeting or inquire about opportunities to collaborate on projects or attend other networking events if appropriate. Regular follow-ups keep the relationship active and demonstrate your ongoing interest in the person's expertise and experiences.

Leveraging Online Platforms

In the digital age, online platforms have become indispensable tools for networking. Professional sites like LinkedIn allow you to connect globally with industry leaders, peers, and potential mentors. When using these platforms, ensure your profile is up-to-date and reflects your professional interests, skills, and accomplishments. Engage actively by sharing relevant articles, commenting on posts, and participating in discussions. This visibility can attract connections that share similar professional interests or value your expertise.

Furthermore, many industries have specific online forums and discussion groups where professionals discuss the latest trends, challenges, and opportunities. Engaging in these forums can enhance your knowledge and establish your reputation as a knowledgeable and proactive professional. When contributing, ensure your comments are thoughtful and add value to the conversation. This approach enriches the discussion and draws positive attention to your professional profile.

Maintaining and Nurturing Professional Relationships

The longevity of your professional relationships can significantly impact your career trajectory. Maintaining these relationships requires more than occasional check-ins; it demands consistent engagement and mutual benefit. Share information and knowledge that will be valuable to your contacts. This could include industry news, research findings, or tools for their professional tasks. Regularly invite connections to networking events or introduce them to other professionals in your network who could provide mutual benefits. This strengthens your existing relationships and fosters a culture of generosity and collaboration within your network.

Celebrate your connections' successes by congratulating them on new jobs, promotions, or other achievements. Support them during challenges by offering help or advice. These gestures contribute to a supportive network that values long-term relationships, ultimately enriching your professional journey with a stable foundation of trusted colleagues and friends.

As you continue to weave this intricate web of professional relationships, remember that each connection has the potential to transform your career in unexpected and rewarding ways. Networking is not just about building a list of contacts; it's about cultivating meaningful relationships that foster mutual growth, support, and success.

Continuous Learning: Keeping Your Skills Sharp in a Rapidly Changing World

In an era where technological advancements and global markets evolve at an unprecedented pace, the concept of education as a finite phase is becoming obsolete. Continuous learning emerges not just as a career advancement strategy but as a necessity for navigating the complexities of today's professional landscape. Updating and expanding your skills can dramatically enhance your adaptability and relevance in any field. Whether you're a software developer needing to stay on top of the latest programming languages or a marketing professional keeping abreast of the newest trends, the ability to learn continuously is a definitive asset in maintaining competitive advantage and career longevity.

Continuous learning extends beyond merely keeping your skills relevant; it also plays a crucial role in broadening your perspectives and fostering personal growth. It encourages a mindset that is curious, proactive, and resilient—qualities that are indispensable in today's fast-paced world. Engaging in ongoing education helps you anticipate changes in your industry and influence and contribute to its evolution. For instance, understanding emerging technologies in your field can position you as a thought leader, opening doors to new opportunities such as speaking engagements, publications, and leadership roles.

Strategies for Lifelong Learning

Adopting a lifelong learning approach can initially seem daunting, especially with time constraints and responsibilities. However, integrating learning into your daily routine can be seamless and enjoyable with the right strategies. Online courses offer a flexible and diverse means of learning new skills or deepening existing knowledge. Platforms like Coursera, Udemy, or LinkedIn Learning provide courses on everything from project management to artificial intelligence, often led by industry experts. Moreover, many of these platforms offer certifications that can enhance your resume and LinkedIn profile.

Workshops and seminars offer more than just learning opportunities; they are platforms for networking and exchanging ideas with peers. Attending these events can provide insights into the practical applications of your new skills and how others in your field are navigating similar challenges. Setting personal projects or challenges related to new skills can be incredibly effective for more self-directed learners. For example, if you are learning graphic design, you might set a goal to design a new logo or poster each week, applying new techniques and tools as you learn them.

Balancing Work and Learning

One of the biggest challenges of continuous learning is finding the time to learn without compromising your work responsibilities. You can achieve this balance by integrating learning into your work tasks wherever possible. For example, if you are learning a new software tool, look for opportunities to use it in your current projects. This helps you improve through practical application and demonstrates your initiative in enhancing your productivity and skill set to your employer.

Time management plays a crucial role here. Dedicate specific times in your schedule for learning, just as you would for any other important activity. Early mornings or lunch breaks can be ideal for short learning sessions, while longer, more in-depth sessions might be scheduled during weekends. It's essential to communicate with your employer about your learning goals. Many organizations offer professional development programs and might even support time off or funding for courses that align with your role.

Leveraging Learning for Career Advancement

Continuous learning can significantly boost your career progression, providing the skills to take on new challenges and advance into higher roles. However, it's not just about accumulating knowledge; it's about applying this learning to benefit your team and organization. Share your new skills and insights with your colleagues. Offer to lead a training session or write a newsletter article about what you've learned and how it can benefit your projects or company operations. This positions you as a proactive and valuable team member and enhances your visibility and reputation within your organization.

Furthermore, consider how each new skill or piece of knowledge helps you build towards your career aspirations. Align your learning objectives with your career goals, ensuring that each new area of expertise brings you closer to where you want to be. Record your learning accomplishments and reflect on their contributions to your professional growth. This record can be invaluable during performance reviews or job interviews, proving your commitment to personal and professional development.

As you navigate the continuous learning curve, remember that each new skill acquired, insight gained, and perspective broadened enhances your professional capabilities and enriches your personal life. In a world that never stops changing, your willingness to keep learning is the most powerful tool you can wield.

Leaving a Legacy: Defining Your Impact and Building Towards It

When you consider the concept of a legacy, it often brings grandiose notions of monumental achievements preserved in the annals of history. However, at its core, a legacy is profoundly personal and uniquely meaningful—it's the footprint you leave on the world, the sum of the impacts you've made in your professional endeavors and personal interactions. Defining the legacy you wish to leave involves introspection and a clear vision of how you want to be remembered. Start by asking yourself key questions: What values do I want to embody? What change do I seek to inspire in my field or community? How do I want to influence the lives of those around me? Your answers will paint a picture of the legacy you aim to build.

Building this legacy requires strategic actions aligned with your defined vision. Goal setting is the first actionable step. These goals should not be seen merely as career objectives or personal milestones but as building blocks of your legacy. For instance, if part of your desired legacy is to innovate within your industry, setting goals related to pioneering research or leading transformative projects can direct your efforts toward this end. Beyond setting goals, assessing your actions' impact is crucial and involves regular reflection on how your activities contribute to or detract from the legacy you aim to create. Are your professional practices and personal behaviors reflecting your core values and advancing your vision?

Community involvement also plays a pivotal role in legacy building. Engaging with community initiatives, mentoring others, or participating in events that promote your field expands your influence and cements your commitment to broader societal contributions. Each interaction in these settings is an opportunity to impart your values, share your vision, and inspire others—actions that weave the fabric of your legacy into the lives of others.

Documenting and sharing your journey is equally important. It allows you to reflect on your own growth and the strides you've made towards your legacy and inspires and guides others. Whether through blogging, writing books, recording podcasts, or even speaking at public engagements, sharing your story can magnify the impact of your experiences. It transforms personal growth into communal inspiration, encouraging others to pursue their paths and perhaps build upon the foundation you've laid.

Documenting and Sharing Your Journey

In today's interconnected world, the power of sharing your journey cannot be overstated. It serves as a personal record of your achievements and reflections and a beacon for others navigating similar paths. Begin by choosing a medium that best suits your style and audience—a professional blog, a social media platform, or more formal publications. Regular updates highlighting your successes and candidly discussing your challenges and failures provide a holistic view of your journey. This authenticity enhances your relatability and reinforces the truth that meaningful legacies are built through perseverance through challenges as much as through celebrated successes.

Moreover, engage with your audience. Respond to comments, participate in discussions, and even seek feedback. This two-way interaction enriches your journey, providing diverse perspectives and fostering a community of learning and mutual growth. Consider collaborating with peers to co-author articles, host discussions, or organize community events. Such collaborations can extend the reach of your legacy, intertwining your efforts with the broader goals of your community or industry.

The role of values in this entire process cannot be overstated. Your core values are the compass that guides your actions and decisions along the path to your legacy. They should resonate through every goal you set, every project you undertake, and every interaction you have. Aligning your actions with your values ensures consistency and integrity in your efforts, strengthening the impact of your legacy. Revisit and reflect on these values regularly to ensure they still represent who you are and aspire to be.

As you build and share your legacy, remember that it is not a static entity but a dynamic one that evolves with you. It is crafted by the goals you achieve, the lives you touch, the community you build, and the values you uphold. Your legacy is your enduring impact on the world—an impact that can continue to resonate long after your direct involvement.

As this chapter on building and sharing your legacy concludes, remember that the essence of legacy lies not in mere memory but in meaningful impact. It is a continuous journey that defines how you are remembered and how you inspire and influence the present and future.

CONCLUSION

As we reach this journey's final pages, I want to reflect on the transformative path we've embarked on together. From the initial understanding of self-help's varied landscape to implementing tangible changes, embracing personal growth, and sustaining these changes for long-term success, this book was intended to guide in crafting a life marked by progress and resilience.

Throughout these chapters, we've examined the essence of habit formation, strategies to overcome procrastination, and the crucial role of consistency. We've explored how unlocking creativity and embracing change are not just concepts but actionable steps that bring us closer to the lives we aspire to lead. Moreover, the power of mindset—fixed versus growth—has underscored every strategy and story shared here.

This book stands out by rejecting the one-size-fits-all approach, emphasizing the importance of personalizing your self-help journey. Each strategy and insight has been presented with the hope that you will tailor it to fit your unique circumstances, needs, and strengths. Remember, the effectiveness of any tool lies not just in its design but in how it is wielded.

I stressed the importance of action over mere inspiration. Motivation, while a beautiful spark, is fleeting; disciplined action and unwavering consistency are the sturdy pillars that will support your journey to lasting change. This approach is backed by science and research, ensuring that the strategies you adopt are not just theories but proven methods of enhancing human lives.

The journey does not end here. I encourage you to continue the practices of self-reflection, adaptability, and lifelong learning. These are not merely chapters in a book but chapters in your life, each with its lessons and growth.

Take the first step today. Use the tools and strategies we've discussed. View each challenge as an opportunity for growth and remember to be resilient in the face of setbacks. Thank you for allowing me to be a part of your journey. I hope this book serves as a catalyst for your transformation, just as the many stories and experiences I have encountered have inspired my continued journey in writing and exploring the intricacies of personal development.

I invite you to join a community of like-minded individuals on their paths to self-improvement. Connect through online forums, social media groups, or local meetups. Share your experiences, challenges, and successes. Community has immense power; together, our journeys can be even more fruitful.

For those eager to explore further, I've listed additional resources at the end of this book, including websites, apps, and books. These resources are extensions of our discussions and will provide deeper insights into specific topics of interest.

In closing, I reflect on this journey of writing and sharing this book. It has been both a challenge and an enrichment, pushing me to synthesize knowledge, question deeply, and articulate clearly. My hope is that it empowers you, as much as it has empowered me, to take control of your narrative and craft a life that resonates with purpose and joy.

Let's continue to grow, learn, and transform. Let the journey go on.

With gratitude and best wishes,

Ivette

SECOND BOOK

THE QUICK GUIDE TO SELF-HELP:

PRACTICAL STRATEGIES FOR PERSONAL GROWTH

INTRODUCTION

Welcome to "The Quick Guide for Self-Help: Practical Strategies for Personal Growth." This guide will discuss practical strategies and techniques for improving your life in several areas and attaining self-development. Whether your goal is to cultivate a resilient mindset, boost productivity, nurture meaningful relationships, or prioritize your well-being, this manual is your companion on the journey toward self-improvement and empowerment.

Life is a journey of self-realization, filled with twists and turns, challenges and triumphs, moments of joy, and moments of sorrow. Along the way, we encounter obstacles that test our resolve, opportunities that expand our horizons, and experiences that shape who we are and aspire to become.

Within the pages of this book lies your road map for traversing the terrain of personal growth with clarity, courage, and conviction. Drawing upon timeless wisdom and practical insights, "The Quick Guide for Self-Help" offers a comprehensive approach to self-improvement, addressing every facet of your being – from understanding yourself and laying the groundwork for success to fostering harmonious relationships and overcoming adversity with resilience and grace.

Each chapter of this guide is meticulously crafted to provide actionable advice and reflective prompts to empower you to take ownership of your growth journey. Whether you embark on a quest to enhance your productivity, cultivate a positive mindset, or heal from past wounds, you will find the tools and inspiration needed to propel you forward on your path to personal fulfillment.

As you turn the pages of this book, I urge you to fully immerse yourself in its transformative wisdom. This is the beginning of the most rewarding adventure of all—the journey of self-awareness and self-discovery. Within these words lies the power to revolutionize your life, unlock your potential, and cultivate a sense of purpose and meaning that surpasses the ordinary.

So, with hearts wide open and minds brimming with curiosity, let's embark on a voyage toward a brighter, more fulfilling future. Your expedition toward personal growth and empowerment starts now.

HOW TO USE THIS GUIDE

Each chapter has particular requests. These are your cues to pull out the journal or notebook and do homework. Write down your answers, honestly. Read the book entirely, and then come back around and continue working on the book and your notes. Immerse yourself. You will find that some of your answers will surprise you. Have patience. Your answers will come.

Chapter 1:
Understanding Yourself

Before embarking on your journey of self-improvement, it's crucial to lay a strong foundation by gaining a deep understanding of yourself. In this chapter, we consider three fundamental aspects of self-awareness that serve as pillars supporting personal growth and development.

First, we explore the realm of values and beliefs, the guiding principles that shape our thoughts, actions, and decisions. By reflecting on your core values and beliefs, you gain clarity on what truly matters to you in life. This self-awareness empowers you to align your goals and aspirations with your values, creating a sense of purpose and fulfillment.

Next, we turn our attention to identifying your strengths and weaknesses. Acknowledging your strengths allows you to leverage them to your advantage, fostering confidence and competence in your endeavors. Similarly, recognizing your weaknesses provides opportunities for growth and development as you work to overcome challenges and expand your skill set. By embracing both your strengths and weaknesses, you cultivate a growth mindset that pushes you toward continuous improvement and success.

Finally, we explore the concept of emotional intelligence, the ability to understand and manage your emotions and empathize with others. Developing emotional intelligence enables you to navigate life's challenges with resilience and empathy, fostering deeper connections and more meaningful relationships. Through self-reflection, mindfulness, and active listening, you cultivate greater self-awareness and emotional resilience, empowering you to thrive personally and professionally.

By delving into these three fundamental aspects of self-awareness—values and beliefs, strengths and weaknesses, and emotional intelligence—you lay the groundwork for a transformative journey of self-discovery and personal growth. Armed with this deep understanding of yourself, you are better equipped to navigate the complexities of life with clarity, confidence, and authenticity.

1. Exploring Your Values and Beliefs

Understanding your values and beliefs provides a solid foundation for making decisions and living a fulfilling life. Values represent what we consider essential and what we live for in life. They combine the core psychological needs of the self and society's norms. Think of values as your personal truth.

Define Your Core Values: Reflect on what matters most to you in life. Are you driven by honesty, social justice, success, or adventure? If you are having difficulty coming up with some values, here is a short list: Financial Security; Compassion; Health/Fitness; Nature; Accomplishment; Creativity; Dependability; Loyalty; Beauty; Bravery; Gratitude; Love; Connection/Relationships; Learning; Leadership; Survival; Self-Preservation; Security; Family; Work; Success; Calm; Freedom.

Examine Your Belief System: Identify the beliefs that shape your thoughts, attitudes, and behaviors. Don't just look at good moments; see what painful memories bring out. Are they empowering or limiting?

2. Identifying Your Strengths and Weaknesses

Knowing your strengths allows you to leverage them for personal and professional success while acknowledging your weaknesses empowers you to grow and improve.

Conduct a SWOT Analysis: Assess your strengths, weaknesses, opportunities, and threats. What are you naturally good at? Where do you struggle?

Make SMART Goals: Ensure your goals are Specific, Measurable, Achievable, Relevant, and Time-bound to increase clarity and effectiveness. (This will come up again)

Seek Feedback: Ask friends, family, and colleagues for honest feedback about your strengths and areas for improvement. This is very important because the way we see ourselves and the way others see us can be quite different.

Create an Action Plan: Break down your goals into smaller, actionable steps, and set deadlines to keep yourself accountable.

3. Cultivating Self-Awareness and Emotional Intelligence

Self-awareness and emotional intelligence are crucial skills for navigating life's challenges and building meaningful relationships. Self-awareness is the conscious knowledge of one's own character, feelings, motives, and desires. Emotional intelligence is the ability to perceive, interpret, demonstrate, control, evaluate, and use emotions to communicate with and relate to others effectively.

Practice Mindfulness: Cultivate present-moment awareness through meditation, deep breathing, or journaling.

Identify Your Emotions: Learn to recognize and label your emotions accurately. What triggers specific emotional responses?

Develop Empathy: Put yourself in others' shoes and strive to understand their perspectives and feelings. How can you respond with compassion and empathy?

Chapter 2:
Setting the Foundation

This chapter serves as a compass, guiding you through the essential steps of defining your life purpose and mission, establishing clear and meaningful goals, and creating a personal development plan to chart your course toward success and fulfillment.

First and foremost, we dive into the exploration of your life purpose and mission. Your life purpose is the underlying reason for your existence, the driving force that gives meaning and direction to your actions and decisions. By reflecting on your passions, values, and aspirations, you gain insight into what truly matters to you and what you hope to achieve in this lifetime. Your mission, on the other hand, is the tangible expression of your purpose—a declaration of the impact you aspire to make in the world. Through introspection and self-discovery, you clarify your purpose and mission, laying the groundwork for a life aligned with your deepest values and aspirations.

Next, we turn our focus to setting clear and meaningful goals. Goals are milestones along your journey, guiding your actions and measuring your progress toward realizing your vision. By employing the SMART criteria—Specific, Measurable, Achievable, Relevant, and Time-bound—you ensure that your goals are concrete, achievable, and aligned with your overarching purpose and mission. Whether your goals pertain to career advancement, personal growth, or relationship enhancement, clarity and specificity are vital to their attainment.

Finally, we explore the creation of a personal development plan to serve as a plan toward success and fulfillment. This plan outlines your actions and strategies to achieve your goals and fulfill your life purpose. It encompasses various areas of self-improvement, including skills development, mindset cultivation, and habit formation. By breaking down your goals into actionable steps, setting deadlines, and allocating resources, you create a clear path forward, empowering you to progress steadily toward your desired outcomes.

Building a fulfilling life begins with establishing a solid foundation rooted in clarity of purpose, meaningful goals, and a strategic plan for personal development. You pave the way for a life of purpose, passion, and fulfillment through introspection, goal setting, and intentional action.

1. Defining Your Life Purpose and Mission

Your life purpose provides direction and meaning, guiding your decisions and actions toward what truly matters to you.

Reflect on Your Passions and Values: What brings you joy and fulfillment? What do you deeply care about?

Consider Your Impact: How do you want to contribute to the world and leave a positive legacy? If this sounds lofty, don't fret. You don't have to solve world hunger to have a positive impact. Think of your children or grandchildren. What kind of memories do you think you are leaving them with? What about your neighbors or coworkers? What would they say about you?

Craft Your Mission Statement: Summarize your life purpose and aspirations into a concise statement that inspires and motivates you. Here is an example: "Our mission is to inspire individuals to discover their purpose and meaning in life, fostering connection, compassion, and personal growth. We aim to cultivate a global community dedicated to living with intention, integrity, and empathy, creating a world of harmony, justice, and abundance for all." (ChatGPT 2024)

2. Establishing Clear and Meaningful Goals

Goals transform your vision into actionable steps, propelling you toward your desired outcomes.

Set SMART Goals: Ensure your goals are Specific, Measurable, Achievable, Relevant, and Time-bound.

Break Down Goals into Milestones: Divide larger goals into smaller, manageable tasks to track progress and stay motivated.

Align Goals with Your Values and Mission: Ensure your goals align with your core values and overarching purpose.

3. Creating a Personal Development Plan

A personal development plan guides your growth and evolution, outlining actionable steps to realize your potential.

Identify Areas for Improvement: Assess your strengths and weaknesses to determine where you can focus your growth efforts.

Set Learning Objectives: Define what skills, knowledge, or habits you want to develop in each area.

Outline Action Steps: Break down each objective into specific actions you can take to make progress.

Establish Accountability and Review Mechanisms: Regularly review your plan, track your progress, and adjust as needed to stay on course.

Chapter 3:
Mastering Your Mindset

Before you dismiss the notion of positive thinking with a skeptical eye roll, let's address a crucial distinction: toxic positivity. Yes, it exists, and we actively steer clear of it. Toxic positivity involves the unrealistic expectation of maintaining a perpetually upbeat attitude, regardless of circumstances, dismissing genuine emotions and struggles as invalid or unworthy of acknowledgment. However, it's essential to recognize that your mindset plays a pivotal role in shaping your perception of the world and influencing your actions and outcomes.

In this chapter, we navigate the delicate balance between fostering a healthy, positive attitude and succumbing to the pitfalls of toxic positivity. We begin by exploring strategies for cultivating a genuine, resilient optimism rooted in authenticity, acceptance, and growth. This involves embracing a mindset of gratitude, cultivating optimism without denying the reality of challenges, and finding silver linings in even the darkest clouds.

Moreover, we look into the complex terrain of overcoming limiting beliefs and self-doubt, those insidious voices that whisper tales of inadequacy and failure. Through introspection and self-awareness, we learn to challenge these beliefs, replacing them with empowering narratives that propel us forward with confidence and conviction.

Furthermore, we equip ourselves with the tools and techniques necessary to develop resilience and mental toughness, enabling us to thrive in the face of adversity. This involves cultivating a growth mindset, reframing setbacks as opportunities for learning and growth, and building emotional resilience to weather life's inevitable storms with grace and resilience.

In essence, this chapter serves as a chart for cultivating an authentic, resilient, and empowering positive attitude. By embracing the principles of genuine positivity, overcoming limiting beliefs, and developing resilience and mental toughness, you pave the way for a life of greater joy, fulfillment, and success, even in the face of life's most formidable challenge.

1. Cultivating a Positive Mindset

A positive mindset empowers you to see opportunities amidst challenges and approach life with optimism and gratitude.

Practice Gratitude: Regularly acknowledge and appreciate the blessings in your life, no matter how small.

Focus on Solutions: Instead of dwelling on problems, focus on finding solutions and taking proactive steps.

Surround Yourself with Positivity: Surround yourself with uplifting people, environments, and media that reinforce optimism.

Practice Gratitude: Start each day by acknowledging what you're grateful for, fostering a positive outlook on life.

Challenge Negative Thoughts: Identify and challenge negative self-talk and limiting beliefs that hold you back from reaching your full potential.

Embrace Failure as Learning: View setbacks as opportunities for growth and learning rather than reasons for discouragement.

Sometimes negativity comes from those we love; we can't just cut them out of our lives. Let them know and understand what you are trying to achieve.

2. Overcoming Limiting Beliefs and Self-Doubt

Limiting beliefs and self-doubt prevents you from reaching your full potential and pursuing your dreams.

Identify Limiting Beliefs: Recognize the beliefs that undermine your confidence and hinder your progress.

Challenge Negative Self-Talk: Replace self-limiting thoughts with empowering affirmations and beliefs.

Take Action Despite Fear: Step out of your comfort zone and take small, manageable risks to build confidence and resilience.

3. Developing Resilience and Mental Toughness

Resilience and mental toughness enable you to bounce back from setbacks and persevere in adversity.

View Setbacks as Learning Opportunities: Embrace failure as a natural part of the learning process and extract valuable lessons from setbacks.

Cultivate Adaptability: Develop the flexibility to adjust to changing circumstances and thrive in unpredictable situations.

Practice Self-Compassion: Treat yourself with kindness and understanding during tough times, recognizing that setbacks don't define your worth.

Chapter 4:
Enhancing Productivity and Time Management

Productivity and time management are not just desirable traits; they are essential skills that are the bedrock of success and personal fulfillment. In this chapter, we embark on a journey to unlock the secrets of mastering these invaluable skills, empowering you to achieve your goals and maximize your potential.

First and foremost, we delve into the art of prioritizing tasks and responsibilities. In a world overflowing with demands and distractions, the ability to discern between what is urgent and what is essential is paramount. Through strategic planning and discernment, you learn to allocate your time and energy to tasks that align with your overarching goals and priorities, ensuring that you make meaningful progress toward your daily objectives.

Next, we confront the perennial nemesis of productivity: procrastination. We explore the root causes of procrastination and develop strategies for overcoming this common obstacle to success. By breaking tasks into smaller, more manageable chunks, setting deadlines, and holding yourself accountable, you liberate yourself from the clutches of procrastination, rekindling your motivation and regaining control over your time and productivity.

Moreover, we address the insidious influence of distractions in our hyper connected world. From social media notifications to the allure of endless scrolling, distractions lurk around every corner, threatening to derail our focus and productivity. Through mindfulness and discipline, we learn to minimize distractions and create an environment conducive to deep work and concentration, maximizing our efficiency and effectiveness in all endeavors.

Finally, we explore techniques for maximizing efficiency and effectiveness in your daily life. From time-blocking and batch processing to the Pomodoro Technique and the Eisenhower Matrix, we equip you with a toolkit of productivity hacks and time management strategies. These will optimize your workflow and give you a sense of accomplishment as you achieve more with less effort.

By mastering the art of productivity and time management, you unlock the key to unlocking your full potential and achieving your loftiest aspirations. You transform your life into a masterpiece of productivity and achievement through strategic prioritization, overcoming procrastination and distractions, and maximizing efficiency and effectiveness.

1. Prioritizing Tasks and Responsibilities

Effective prioritization allows you to focus your time and energy on activities that align with your goals and values.

Identify Important Tasks: Determine which tasks impact your long-term objectives most and prioritize them accordingly.

Use Prioritization Techniques: Employ methods such as the Eisenhower Matrix or ABCDE method to categorize tasks based on their urgency and importance.

Set Clear Deadlines: Establish task deadlines to create a sense of urgency and accountability.

2. Managing Procrastination and Distractions

Procrastination and distractions can derail your productivity and prevent you from accomplishing your goals.

Understand the Root Causes: Identify the underlying reasons for procrastination, such as fear of failure, perfectionism, or lack of motivation.

Break Tasks into Smaller Steps: Divide larger tasks into smaller, more manageable chunks to reduce getting overwhelmed and make progress more attainable.

Minimize Distractions: Eliminate or minimize distractions such as social media, emails, and noise to create a conducive work environment.

3. Maximizing Efficiency and Effectiveness

Efficiency and effectiveness go hand in hand, allowing you to achieve more in less time while maintaining quality.

Utilize Time Management Techniques: Implement strategies like time blocking, the Pomodoro Technique, or batching similar tasks to optimize your workflow.

Streamline Processes: Identify inefficiencies in your routines and workflows and seek ways to streamline or automate repetitive tasks.

Delegate When Possible: Delegate tasks that others can handle, freeing up your time and energy for higher-priority activities.

Chapter 5:
Nurturing Relationships

Healthy and fulfilling relationships are the cornerstone of our emotional well-being and overall happiness. In this chapter, we set out on a journey to deepen our understanding of the dynamics underpinning strong connections, effective communication, conflict resolution, and boundary-setting, all of which are essential for nurturing positive and harmonious relationships.

First and foremost, we explore the art of building solid connections. Genuine relationships are built on trust, empathy, and mutual respect. Through active listening, compassion, and vulnerability, we cultivate authentic connections that transcend surface-level interactions, fostering intimacy and understanding.

Next, we delve into the intricacies of effective communication. Communication lies at the heart of every successful relationship, serving as the bridge that connects individuals and fosters connection. We explore techniques for expressing ourselves openly and honestly while also practicing active listening and empathy to truly understand the perspectives of others.

Moreover, we confront the inevitable conflicts that arise in any relationship. Conflict is a natural part of human interaction, but it need not be destructive. By embracing conflict as an opportunity for growth and understanding, we learn to navigate disagreements with grace and kindness, finding mutually beneficial solutions that strengthen our relationships.

In addition, we discuss the importance of maintaining healthy boundaries. Boundaries are essential for preserving our well-being and autonomy within relationships. We explore strategies for setting and enforcing boundaries effectively, communicating our needs and limitations with clarity and assertiveness while also respecting the boundaries of others.

This chapter serves as a blueprint for cultivating healthy and fulfilling relationships that enrich our lives and contribute to our overall happiness and well-being. Through building sturdy connections, effective communication, conflict resolution, and boundary-setting, we create a foundation of trust, understanding, and mutual support that sustains us through life's challenges and triumphs.

1. Building Healthy and Fulfilling Relationships

Meaningful relationships enrich our lives and provide support, companionship, and a sense of belonging.

Invest Time and Effort: Prioritize spending quality time with loved ones and nurturing your connections through shared experiences and meaningful interactions.

Show Empathy and Understanding: Practice active listening and empathy, seeking to understand others' perspectives and feelings without judgment.

Cultivate Trust and Respect: Build trust and respect through honesty, reliability, and consistency in your words and actions.

Communicate Effectively: Express your thoughts and feelings openly and respectfully, and encourage open communication in your interactions with others.

2. Effective Communication and Conflict Resolution

Clear and open communication is essential for resolving conflicts and maintaining healthy relationships.

Practice Active Listening: Listen attentively to others' concerns and perspectives and validate their feelings before expressing your own.

Express Yourself Assertively: Communicate your thoughts, feelings, and needs assertively and respectfully, avoiding blame or criticism.

Resolve Conflicts Constructively: Approach conflicts as opportunities for growth and understanding, seeking mutually beneficial solutions through compromise and collaboration.

3. Setting Boundaries and Maintaining balance

Setting boundaries is crucial for preserving your well-being and maintaining healthy relationships. Establishing healthy boundaries protects your well-being and maintains balance in your relationships.

Know Your Limits: Identify and communicate your personal boundaries clearly and assertively to others.

Respect Others' Boundaries: Honor and respect others' boundaries, recognizing their autonomy and right to self-care.

Prioritize Self-Care: Place self-care at the top of your list, taking time to recharge and nurture your physical, emotional, and mental well-being, ensuring you have the energy and capacity to show up fully in your relationships.

Chapter 6:
Achieving Balance and Well-Being

Attaining balance and well-being is not merely a luxury but a fundamental necessity for experiencing a life of purpose and fulfillment. In this chapter, we embark on a journey to uncover the myriad strategies that enable us to prioritize self-care, effectively manage stress, nurture our physical health and wellness, and harmonize the diverse facets of our lives.

First and foremost, we delve into the art of self-care and stress management. In our fast-paced and often demanding world, nurturing our mental, emotional, and physical well-being is indispensable for maintaining equilibrium and resilience. Through mindfulness practices, relaxation techniques, and boundary-setting, we learn to cultivate a sense of inner peace and balance, even amidst life's inevitable challenges and stressors.

Next, we explore the critical role of physical health and wellness in achieving overall well-being. Our bodies are the vessels through which we experience life, and prioritizing our physical health is essential for vitality and longevity. We delve into strategies for nourishing our bodies with nutritious foods, engaging in regular exercise, and prioritizing rest and recovery to optimize our physical well-being and vitality.

Achieving balance requires juggling multiple responsibilities and priorities, from work and family to hobbies and personal pursuits. Through intentional goal-setting, time management, and boundary-setting, we strive to create a life aligned with our values and aspirations, allowing us to experience fulfillment and satisfaction in all areas of our lives.

This chapter serves as instructions for cultivating balance and well-being in our lives—a journey that encompasses self-care, stress management, physical health, and harmonious living. By embracing these strategies, we empower ourselves to lead lives that are not only fulfilling and meaningful but also sustainable and resilient, enabling us to thrive in every aspect of our existence.

1. Practicing Self-Care and Stress Management

Self-care is the foundation of well-being. It enables us to manage stress effectively and nurture our mental, emotional, and physical health.

Prioritize Self-Care Activities: Identify activities that recharge and rejuvenate you, such as meditation, exercise, hobbies, or spending time in nature.

Set Boundaries: Learn to say no to commitments that drain your energy and create overwhelm, prioritizing your own needs and well-being.

Practice Stress Management Techniques: Incorporate relaxation techniques like deep breathing, mindfulness, or journaling into your daily routine to reduce stress and promote inner peace.

2. Cultivating Physical Health and Wellness

Physical health is interconnected with mental and emotional well-being, contributing to our overall quality of life and vitality.

Maintain a Balanced Diet: Fuel your body with nutritious foods rich in vitamins, minerals, and antioxidants, and stay hydrated to support optimal health.

Incorporate Regular Exercise: Engage in physical activity that you enjoy, whether walking, swimming, yoga, or strength training, to boost your mood and energy levels.

Get Adequate Rest and Sleep: Prioritize quality sleep by establishing a consistent bedtime routine and creating a restful sleep environment to support optimal rest and recovery.

3. Finding Harmony in Work, Life, and Leisure

Achieving a balance between work, personal life, and leisure activities is crucial for overall well-being and satisfaction.

Set Boundaries Between Work and Personal Life: Create clear boundaries between work and leisure time, ensuring you have time for relaxation, hobbies, and spending quality time with loved ones.

Prioritize Leisure and Recreation: Make time for activities that bring you joy and fulfillment, whether pursuing hobbies, spending time outdoors, or engaging in creative pursuits.

Practice Mindfulness and Presence: Cultivate mindfulness in your daily life, savoring each moment and focusing on the present rather than dwelling on past regrets or future worries.

Chapter 7:
Overcoming Challenges and Adversity

Life presents many challenges and adversities, each testing the depths of our resilience and character. However, it is not the challenges that define us but our response to them that shapes our journey. This chapter explores the transformative power of resilience and adaptation in the face of life's trials.

First and foremost, we dig into the art of embracing change and adaptability. Change is an inevitable part of life, and our ability to adapt to new circumstances and challenges is crucial for growth and fulfillment. Through practices such as mindfulness, flexibility, and openness to new experiences, we learn to navigate change with grace and resilience, embracing it as an opportunity for personal evolution and expansion.

Next, we confront the lingering impact of past trauma and emotional wounds. Traumatic experiences can leave lasting scars on our psyche, hindering our ability to live fully and authentically. Through introspection, self-compassion, and therapeutic techniques, we embark on a journey of healing and restoration, reclaiming our power and agency in the process.

Moreover, we explore the profound wisdom inherent in turning setbacks into opportunities for growth and resilience. Setbacks and failures are inevitable in the human experience but need not define us. By reframing challenges as opportunities for learning and development, we cultivate resilience and tenacity, emerging more robust and resilient than before.

This chapter serves as a testament to the indomitable spirit of the human soul—a spirit capable of transcending adversity and transforming hardship into triumph. Through embracing change and adaptability, healing past trauma, and turning setbacks into opportunities for growth, we empower ourselves to navigate life's challenges with courage, resilience, and grace.

1. Embracing Change and Adaptability

Change is inevitable, and our ability to adapt to it determines our resilience and success in navigating life's twists and turns.

Cultivate a Growth Mindset: Embrace change as an opportunity for learning and personal growth rather than fearing it as a threat.

Practice Flexibility: Stay open to new possibilities and perspectives, adapting your plans and expectations as circumstances evolve.

Focus on What You Can Control: Shift your focus from what you can't control to what you can influence, taking proactive steps to navigate change with resilience and grace.

2. Resolving Past Trauma and Healing Emotional Wounds

Past traumas and emotional wounds can weigh us down and hinder our ability to thrive in the present. Healing is a journey of self-discovery and self-compassion.

Acknowledge Your Pain: Allow yourself to acknowledge and validate your emotions, honoring the significance of your experiences.

Seek Support: Reach out to trusted friends, family members, or mental health professionals for support and guidance in processing your emotions and experiences.

Practice Self-Compassion: Be gentle and patient with yourself as you navigate the healing process, recognizing that healing takes time and effort.

3. Turning Setbacks into Opportunities for Growth

Setbacks and failures are inevitable but can also serve as valuable lessons and catalysts for personal growth and transformation.

Reframe Failure as Feedback: Instead of viewing setbacks as signs of incompetence or unworthiness, see them as opportunities for learning and improvement.

Extract Lessons and Insights: Reflect on the lessons and insights gained from setbacks, identifying areas for growth and development.

Take Action Towards Growth: Use setbacks as motivation to take positive action towards your goals, leveraging newfound resilience and determination to overcome obstacles.

Chapter 8:
Mark Your Achievements

Sustaining growth and fulfillment is not merely a destination to reach but rather an ongoing journey that demands unwavering dedication, profound self-awareness, and a steadfast commitment to continuous improvement. As we step into this final chapter, we delve into the timeless wisdom and practical strategies that will guide us in nurturing and maintaining our journey toward lasting success and fulfillment.

First and foremost, we celebrate the milestones that mark our progress along the path of personal growth and achievement. These milestones are beacons of inspiration, reminding us how far we've come and fueling our determination to continue. Through reflection and celebration, we honor our accomplishments and acknowledge the hard work and perseverance that have brought us to this point.

We cultivate gratitude and mindfulness as indispensable companions on our journey. Gratitude opens our hearts to the abundance and beauty surrounding us, fostering a sense of contentment and fulfillment in our daily lives. On the other hand, mindfulness anchors us in the present moment, allowing us to savor the richness of each experience and cultivate a deeper connection with ourselves and the world around us.

Finally, we reaffirm our commitment to self-improvement, recognizing that growth is a lifelong endeavor that requires dedication and perseverance. We commit to embracing new challenges, stepping outside our comfort zones, and embracing the discomfort of growth with courage and resilience. Through continuous learning, reflection, and refinement, we ensure that our journey toward success and fulfillment remains vibrant, dynamic, and deeply meaningful.

This final chapter serves as a rallying cry—a call to arms for all who seek to live a life of purpose, passion, and fulfillment. By celebrating milestones, cultivating gratitude and mindfulness, and committing to the journey of self-improvement, we lay the groundwork for a future filled with boundless opportunities and infinite possibilities. So, let us embrace this journey with open hearts and steadfast determination, knowing that the best is yet to come.

1. Celebrating Milestones and Acknowledging Progress

Celebrating milestones and acknowledging progress is essential for maintaining motivation and momentum on your journey of personal growth.

Reflect on Achievements: Take time to reflect on your accomplishments, both big and small, and celebrate your progress.

Set Milestones and Rewards: Break down larger goals into smaller milestones and reward yourself for reaching each milestone, reinforcing positive behavior and motivation.

Share Successes with Others: Share your achievements with friends, family, or mentors, inviting them to celebrate your successes and share your joy.

2. Cultivating Gratitude and Mindfulness

Practicing gratitude and mindfulness fosters a more profound appreciation for life's blessings and cultivates inner peace and contentment.

Keep a Gratitude Journal: Regularly write down things you're grateful for, no matter how small, to cultivate a mindset of abundance and appreciation.

Practice Mindfulness Meditation: Set aside time daily to practice mindfulness meditation, focusing on the present moment with non-judgmental awareness and acceptance.

Savor the Simple Pleasures: Slow down and savor the simple pleasures of life, such as a beautiful sunset, a warm cup of tea, or a heartfelt conversation with a loved one.

3. Continuing the Journey of Self-Improvement

The journey of self-improvement is lifelong, requiring a commitment to growth, learning, and self-discovery.

Set New Goals and Challenges: Continuously set new goals and challenges that stretch your limits and inspire you to grow and evolve.

Seek Learning and Development Opportunities: Never stop learning and seeking new knowledge and skills that enrich your life and expand your horizons.

Embrace Feedback and Reflection: Welcome feedback from others as an opportunity for growth and self-awareness, and regularly reflect on your experiences and lessons learned.

CONCLUSION

Congratulations on completing "The Quick Guide to Self-Help: Practical Strategies for Personal Growth"! You have embarked on a transformative journey towards self-improvement and personal development by integrating the practical strategies and techniques shared within these pages.

As you move forward, remember that pursuing growth and fulfillment is not a static destination but a dynamic, ongoing process of self-discovery and evolution. Embracing this journey entails celebrating your achievements, practicing gratitude and mindfulness, and committing to continuous self-improvement.

Central to this journey is cultivating balance and well-being, which requires intentional effort and self-awareness. By mastering your mindset, taking control of your time, and honing the principles of effective communication and relationship-building, you have laid a sturdy foundation for personal growth and success.

As you venture forth, do so with an open heart and a spirit of curiosity, fully aware of the immense potential for growth and self-discovery that lies within you. Embrace the challenges and triumphs that await, for they are the catalysts that will propel you toward the best version of yourself.

In this grand adventure of self-discovery, may you find purpose, joy, and fulfillment and continue striving to become the architect of your destiny. Remember, the power to shape your life is not just a possibility but a reality. With each conscious choice you make, you are not just sculpting a future but creating a masterpiece brimming with opportunities and promise.

REFERENCES

Nurturing the Mind: A Journey to Wholeness in Wellness and Mental Health - Beldum. https://beldum.org/nurturing-the-mind-a-journey-to-wholeness-in-wellness-and-mental-health/

How Can Life Coaching Help Me Clarify My Goals and Priorities? - Creed Branson. https://creedbranson.com/how-can-life-coaching-help-me-clarify-my-goals-and-priorities-2/

The Power of Self-Reflection: Enhancing Self-Awareness and Personal De – Moore Health & Wellness L.L.C.. https://moorewellnessgroup.com/blogs/feel-good-monday/the-power-of-self-reflection-enhancing-self-awareness-and-personal-development

The Path to Progress: Fostering Self-Awareness for Personal Development — Transcontinental Times. https://www.transcontinentaltimes.com/cultivating-self-awareness-personal/

How Can Life Coaching Help Me Clarify My Goals and Priorities? - Creed Branson. https://creedbranson.com/how-can-life-coaching-help-me-clarify-my-goals-and-priorities-2/

The Art of Goal Setting: Defining and Attaining Career Milestones - River. https://www.riversoftware.com/career-development/the-art-of-goal-setting-defining-and-attaining-career-milestones/

The Power of Adaptation: Embracing Change in a Fast-Paced World - Aquafresh Prime.
https://www.aquafreshprime.com/automobile/the-power-of-adaptation-embracing-change-in-a-fast-paced-world/

Author: OpenAI Title: ChatGPT-3.5 Publisher: OpenAI URL: https://chatgpt.com/c/4fcea70a-3bb4-4e7d-8fdd-c23cdf95ba33, 5/9/2024

THIRD BOOK

THE BIPOLAR JOURNEY

PRACTICAL STRATEGIES FOR DAILY LIFE, SELF-CARE, OVERCOMING STIGMA AND LIVING BOLDLY

INTRODUCTION

The day I was diagnosed with bipolar disorder, I was sitting in a stark, off-white room with mahogany furniture that seemed far too bright, even though it was just like every other military hospital Senior Doctor's office. His words felt like they were dropped from a great height, smashing into my reality with the subtlety of a wrecking ball. I remember thinking, "Well, this is a new brand of Monday; my career is over." There was confusion, a creeping dread, but oddly, a sliver of relief too. Finally, there was a name for the chaos that had been my constant companion. I finally could explain the refinishing of furniture at 3 AM, or rearranging the living room furniture for no reason, skipping out on work, the shopping and spending sprees, the hyper sexuality, the driving recklessly, and, of course, the depths of despair and agony at the thought that tomorrow would be another day if I were unlucky enough to wake up...

This book is born from these moments and countless others that followed. It's crafted to tell a story and be a companion on your journey. If you've just been handed a bipolar diagnosis or have been wrestling with it for years and are looking for fresh perspectives, this is for you. My aim? To light a path through the fog of fear and misinformation, to offer you hope and practical strategies, and to remind you fervently that this diagnosis does not define you. It's a part of your life, not the end of it.

I'm not a psychiatrist or psychologist. I don't wear a white coat, and my name doesn't follow with a string of impressive letters. But I have been where you are now. I've navigated the rocky terrains of this condition for over 30 years, and if there's one thing I've learned, it's that experience can be just as valuable as a medical degree. I'm here to share that experience with you—to offer insights from clinical studies and living a life full of ups and downs, victories and setbacks.

In these pages, we will explore the nooks and crannies of bipolar disorder—from deciphering the symptoms to managing medications and their side effects. We'll talk about the adjustments you might need to make to your lifestyle and how to handle the relationships that might feel more fragile now. And we'll do all of this with humor and light-heartedness because sometimes, laughter truly is the best medicine.

You're not alone on this path. This book is your invitation to a conversation, sharing stories and strategies that I hope will empower you. Together, we'll demystify the stigmas, tackle the hard questions, and find ways to explain your diagnosis without sending people running for the hills.

Let's not just survive with bipolar disorder; let's live with it, and let's live well. With actionable advice grounded in the latest research and my own life lessons, I promise to offer you tools that can make a real difference. Engage with this book, reflect on your experiences, and apply what resonates with your journey.

So, take a deep breath. You've got this, and I'm here to help. Let's redefine what it means to live with bipolar disorder, turning fear into knowledge and knowledge into power. Here's to finding light in unexpected places, and here's to you—more resilient and hopeful than you ever imagined possible.

CHAPTER:1
DECODING BIPOLAR: BEYOND THE DIAGNOSIS

Have you ever had one of those days where everything seems to flip upside-down? Well, getting diagnosed with bipolar disorder can feel a bit like that, but with a plot twist, you didn't see coming. You are the main character in a mystery novel, trying to decipher clues about your brain! Here we'll unravel some of those mysteries together, pulling back the curtain on the enigmatic world of bipolar disorder. From understanding the basics to getting a grip on the diagnosis process, consider this an insider's guide to navigating the stormy weather with a bit of humor and a lot of heart.

1.1 Bipolar Basics: Symptoms, Types, and Diagnosis

Understanding Symptoms

First things first, talk about symptoms. If bipolar disorder were a duo, its lead singers would be Mania and Depression, each rocking their unique style. Mania isn't just about feeling a bit energetic, it's like being on a caffeine buzz that won't quit. You might feel euphoric, full of grand plans, or irritably unstoppable. Then there's its counterpart, Depression. This isn't just a lousy day; it's like wading through molasses while wearing lead boots, with overwhelming sadness and fatigue and sometimes feeling hopelessly empty.

In the middle, playing a less intense set is Hypomania Mania's younger sibling. It's similar to mania but dialed down. You won't be scaling skyscrapers, but you might buzz with more energy than usual, which can feel either exhilarating or a bit out of control. Recognizing these symptoms in yourself or your loved ones can be like putting glasses on for the first time—suddenly, the blur becomes clear.

Classifying Bipolar Disorder

Now, onto the types—because not all bipolar disorders are created equal, we have Bipolar I, where mania takes the main stage for at least a week or is severe enough to need hospital care. There's Bipolar II, where hypomania plays the opening act, followed by significant bouts of depression. Let's not forget about Cyclothymic Disorder, featuring at least two years of repeated mood changes, swinging from hypomanic symptoms to depressive symptoms without hitting full-blown highs or lows.

Getting these classifications right is crucial because every detail counts, just like any good thriller. Misclassifying can lead to the wrong management strategies, turning an already bumpy ride into an amusement park ride.

The Diagnosis Process

So, how do you pin down something as slippery as a bipolar diagnosis? Not through a simple blood test or a magic quiz. Diagnosis is more of an art form mixed with science. It typically starts with a comprehensive clinical interview by a mental health professional playing detective, gathering clues from your symptoms, medical history, and often input from family. Sometimes, they'll run tests to rule out other culprits like thyroid issues or to check medication levels. It's detective work, with you as the key witness.

Importance of Accurate Diagnosis

Why the fuss over getting the diagnosis spot-on? Well, think of it as getting the correct key for a lock. A precise diagnosis opens the door to effective management. It helps tailor the right treatment plan, whether medication, therapy, or lifestyle changes, ensuring that interventions are as effective as possible. An accurate diagnosis also helps set the stage for what to expect in your personal and professional life, paving the way for a clearer understanding of your experiences and needs.

Navigating the waters of bipolar disorder starts with understanding its fundamentals, cycles, and triggers. Knowledge makes you better equipped to advocate for yourself and make informed decisions. Remember, knowledge isn't just power it's empowerment. Let's put on those detective hats and continue to decode the mysteries of bipolar disorder together.

1.2 The Science Behind Bipolar: Neurobiology Made Simple

Imagine your brain is like a bustling city—neurons are the citizens, neurotransmitters are the messages they send each other, and the city's infrastructure is the brain's structure. In the world of bipolar disorder, this city experiences severe electrical storms (manic episodes) and power outages (depressive episodeLet'set's simplify this complex neurobiology without needing a PhD to understand it.

Brain Chemistry and Bipolar

In the brain's dynamic hub, neurotransmitters like serotonin, dopamine, and norepinephrine are the primary messengers that communicate mood, energy levels, and emotional well-being. Think of dopamine as the brain's caffeine – it gets you up and running, fuels your highs, and, in excess, might make you feel like you're operating at warp speed during manic episodes. On the flip side, when there's a drop in this and other neurotransmitters like serotonin, it's akin to the coffee running out before your day does, potentially ushering in a period of depression.

In bipolar disorder, the regulation of these neurotransmitters gets skewed. The result? A neurological seesaw that swings between the extremes of emotional highs and lows. This imbalance isn't just about feeling good or bad, but a profound disturbance in the brain's natural rhythm, which affects overall functioning.

Research Insights

Recent studies have thrown a spotlight on the complexity of bipolar disorder, debunking myths that it's just a mood swing thing that can be snapped out of. Advanced imaging studies show that some regions of the brain might be structurally and functionally different in those with bipolar disorder compared to those without. For instance, areas like the prefrontal cortex – the brain's command center for decision-making, judgment, and problem-solving – often show variations in activity. This insight helps explain why someone with bipolar disorder might make impulsive decisions during a manic episode or struggle to make any decisions during a depressive phase.

Moreover, research utilizing functional MRI (fMRI) has observed how the brain behaves during tasks involving emotional processing, revealing distinctive patterns in people with bipolar disorder. These groundbreaking insights are crucial as they guide the development of more targeted treatments beyond symptom management to address the root neurological issues.

Genes vs. Environment

The age-old debate of nature versus nurture also plays a significant role in bipolar disorder. Genetically, if bipolar disorder were a novel, it would be a saga filled with complex characters; multiple genes contribute to the risk, each adding their twist to the plot. No single gene "causes" bipolar disorder, but the interaction of many genes can significantly increase the likelihood of developing the condition.

Environmentally, think of your life experiences as the weather affecting that bustling city in your brain. Certain life events or stressors, like relationship troubles, loss of a loved one, or extreme stress, might not cause bipolar disorder directly but can trigger its onset in someone already genetically predisposed. These experiences flip a switch, and the city's usual operations spiral into electrical storms or power outages.

Future Directions

Looking ahead, the horizon is promising in bipolar disorder research. Scientists are delving into not only the genetic and environmental causes but also revolutionary treatments that could more precisely recalibrate the brain's faulty wiring. One exciting frontier is personalized medicine, driven by genetic testing, which tailors treatments to individual patients, potentially enhancing treatment efficacy and reducing side effects.

Furthermore, ongoing research into brain plasticity offers hope that even with a genetic predisposition, the brain can learn new patterns of activity that promote stability rather than extremes of mood. Potential biomarkers are also being explored, which could lead to earlier detection and intervention, shifting the narrative from crisis management to prevention and maintenance.

Understanding the neurobiology of bipolar disorder sets the stage for more effective interventions and significantly shifts the narrative from blame and misunderstanding to one of empathy and precision in care. As we continue to unravel the intricate tapestry of brain function, genetics, and environmental impacts, the future looks increasingly hopeful for those affected by bipolar disorder, providing clarity and new tools to manage and thrive despite the challenges.

1.3 Debunking Myths: What Bipolar Disorder Isn't

Let's set the record straight on a few things. If confusion were a sport, the myths surrounding bipolar disorder would have a pretty good shot at taking home the gold. From wild misconceptions to oversimplified stereotypes, it's high time we tackled this head-on because understanding what bipolar disorder isn't is just as crucial as understanding what it is.

Myth vs. Reality

First up, the classic mix-up: "Bipolar means split personality." Nope, not even close. Bipolar disorder is about experiencing significant mood swings that include emotional highs (mania or hypomania) and lows (depression), not having two distinct personalities. This common misunderstanding might stem from the word "bipolar," suggesting a split between two poles or extremes, let's be clear—this is about variations in mood, not identity.

Then there's the big one: "People with bipocan'tan't lead normal lives." Now, this is not only false but also incredibly dismissive. Sure, managing bipolar disorder presents its unique set of challenges, but with. Still, with the proper treatment and strategies, many people with bipolar disorder hold down fulfilling jobs, maintain healthy relationships, and lead rich, productive livIt'sIt's not about livin' a 'no'mal' liit'sit's about living your life and living it well, regardless of a diagnosis.

Stigma and Misunderstandings

Speaking of misconceptions, the stigma around bipolar disorder can feel like a pesky shadow you can't shake. This stigma stems mainly from a lack of understanding and loads of misinformation. People h"ar "bip"lar" and think of unpredictability, instability, or worse, unreliability. This stigma can lead to people with bipolar disorder feeling isolated, misunderstood, and even discriminated against, which can prevent them from seeking the help they need.

Challenging, educating, and shining a light on these shadows is crucial. By speaking openly about what bipolar disorder is, sharing stories, and spreading accurate information, we can chip away at the misconceptions and make it easier for people to seek support without fear of judgment.

Bipolar Disorder and Violence

Now let's tackle a particularly damaging myth: the idea that bipolar disorder inherently leads to violent behavior. Studies consistently show that most people with mental health conditions, including bipolar disorder, are no more violent than the general population. They are more likely to be victims of violence than perpetrators. It's essential to look at these statistics head-on to dismantle the baseless fears that can surround mental health diagnoses. This isn't just about correcting false information; it's about changing how society perceives and treats those with bipolar disorder.

The Role of Media

Lastly, let's talk about the elephant in the room—the media. Films, TV shows, and even news reports can sometimes paint those with bipolar disorder as caricatures—unpredictable, over-the-top, or tragic figures. While there's been some progress in recent years, with more nuanced portrayals and greater sensitivity, there's still a long way to go. The media influences perceptions and can be a formidable ally in educating the public and combating stigma.

Take, for instance, a popular TV show that portrays a character with bipolar disorder. If the character is well-rounded, their condition accurately represented, and their challenges met with empathy and support from others, it can foster understanding and compassion in the audience. On the flip side, sensationalized or inaccurate portrayals can reinforce stereotypes and widen the gap of misunderstanding.

When we encounter these portrayals in our everyday lives, it's valuable to engage critically, questioning and discussing their accuracy and impact. Whether writing a thoughtful blog post, sharing insights on social media, or simply discussing it with friends and family, every conversation can be a step towards greater understanding.

As we continue to pull apart the myths and shine a light on the realities, remember it's about fostering empathy, challenging stereotypes, and creating a more informed and understanding society. Whether you're living with bipolar disorder or know someone who is, the power of knowledge and the strength of a community can make all the difference. Let's keep the conversation going, debunk myths, and build bridges of understanding, one truth at a time.

1.4 Bipolar I vs. Bipolar II: Navigating the Differences

Ah, the tale of two bipolar. When you first hear about Bipolar I and II, it might sound like a sequel in a film franchise—when you thought you understood the plot, along comes a twist! However, understanding these types is crucial in managing the condition effectively. Let's break it down: Bipolar I is the blockbuster of the series, known for its full-blown manic episodes. These aren't just spurts of high energy or enthusiasm; we're talking about intense, week-long (at least) escapades where sleep becomes a forgotten concept, decisions are made at the speed of light, and grand, often unrealistic plans are set into motion. To meet the criteria for Bipolar I, a person must have experienced at least one of these manic episodes, which episodes of depression might follow. However, the latter isn't a requirement for diagnosis.

Conversely, Bipolar II might be seen as the less intense sequel, but trust me, it's no less impactful. It features hypomania, a milder form of mania that's not as extreme or potentially disruptive as full mania. People experiencing hypomania can often still go about their daily routines. However, the catch with Bipolar II is the significant periods of depression that tag along. These episodes are frequently more profound, longer, and more disabling than those experienced in Bipolar I.

There is a third category, sometimes referred to as Bipolar III. It is cyclothymia, and the episodes are not as extreme as those in bipolar I or II. Now, why does this matter? Picture this: you're trying to solve a problem, if you have the wrong formula the results will not be accurate. It helps immensely to know what you're dealing with. Treating Bipolar I with strategies better suited for Bipolar II (or vice versa) can be like using a screwdriver on a nail—technically possible, but unnecessarily frustrating and ineffective. For Bipolar I, treatment often prioritizes controlling the highs of mania and might include a combination of mood stabilizers and antipsychotic medications. The approach is somewhat aggressive because unchecked mania can lead to risky behaviors and significant life disruptions.

Treatment for Bipolar II, meanwhile, tends to focus heavily on managing depression while keeping an eye on the milder hypomanic episodes. This might involve a different balance of medications, like using antidepressants with mood stabilizers to prevent a swing into hypomanIt'sIt's a delicate dance, requiring precise tunes and steps to maintain the right rhythm.

Living with each type of bipolar disorder also dishes out its unique set of daily challenges and strategies. With Bipolar I, the unpredictability of manic episodes can feel like walking a tightrope without knowing when the wind might gust. Strategies here often involve strict adherence to medication schedules, regular therapy sessions, and developing a strong awareness of one's mood shifts to mitigate the mania before it takes the stage; it's about prevention, preparation, and quick action.

For those managing Bipolar II, the long shadows of depression make it crucial to have robust support systems and coping mechanisms in play, so it's less about bracing for the occasional storm and more about continually nurturing one's mental garden to keep the weeds of depression from taking root. This might mean regular exercise, maintaining a consistent sleep schedule, and perhaps most importantly, staying connected with supportive friends, family, or support groups who can provide light during darker times.

Navigating Bipolar I and II requires not just knowledge but also patience and personalization in treatment and lifestyle adjustments. Each type has its traits, challenges, and nuances, making it essential to tailor your approach—be it through medication, therapy, or daily habits—to suit the specific type you or your loved one is dealing with. Understanding these differences enables better management, smoother sailing, and a more stable life despite the ups and downs. So, while the differences between Bipolar I and II can be subtle, they are incredibly significant in crafting a life that acknowledges the highs and lows but isn't defined by them. And with the proper knowledge and tools at your disposal, navigating these waters becomes a part of the adventure, not the whole story.

1.5 The Role of Genetics and Environment in Bipolar Disorder

Let's talk about what's brewing in your genetic cocktail and how your environment plays a role in the mix. It's like understanding the recipe that makes up your unique flavor of bipolar disorder. You might think that genes are the all-powerful directors behind the scenes, while your environment is just the stage setting.

But in reality, it's way more interactive—think of it as a dynamic play where genes and environment constantly improvise.

Genetic Factors

Diving into the pool of genetics, it's clear that bipolar disorder doesn't play favorites; it tends to run in families, suggesting a solid genetic thread. Research pinpoints that if you have a relative with bipolar disorder, your likelihood of developing the condition is higher. However, it's not a straightforward inheritance like passing down a family heirloom. It's more like a lottery—having the genes increases your chances but doesn't guarantee the jackpot of developing the disorder.

Scientists have been mapping the human genome and found several genes that are more common in populations with bipolar disorder. These genes often play crucial roles in the brain's communication systems. Also, it's not just one single gene at fault here; it's more likely a team effort with multiple genes, each adding its own little twist to how bipolar disorder manifests in an individual. This complexity is why predicting or preventing the disorder using genetic information alone isn't currently feasible. However, understanding these genetic influences helps us grasp why bipolar disorder can appear in different shades and intensities in other people.

Environmental Triggers

Now let's set the stage with environmental factors. These are the life experiences and external conditions that can trigger the onset of bipolar disorder symptoms or influence the course of the disorder. Common triggers include stressful life events like the loss of a loved one, a breakup, or significant career changes. Even seemingly positive stressors, like getting married or starting a new job, can spark symptoms if they shake up your world significantly.

Imagine your genetic predisposition as a loaded spring. Environmental stressors are like weights added to that spring. Add enough weight, and the spring might snap, triggering the onset of bipolar disorder symptoms. This analogy helps explain why two people with similar genetic risks might have different experiences; it all depends on the weights added to their respective springs.

Nature vs. Nurture Debate

The age-old debate of nature versus nurture is particularly poignant in bipolar disorder. It's not about whether genetics or environment are more important; it's about how they interact. Think of it as a dance between your internal genetic makeup and external life experiences. Sometimes, genetics take the lead; other times, environmental factors dictate the next move. This dance can determine the onset, severity, and very nature of the disorder in an individual.

For instance, someone might carry the genetic predisposition for bipolar disorder but remain symptom-free until they encounter severe psychological stress or substance abuse, which then triggers the condition. On the other hand, someone with less genetic risk might experience the same stressors but never develop bipolar disorder. This interplay suggests that while you can't change your genetics, managing your environment and how you respond to stress can significantly influence disorder'ser's impact on your life.

Family History and Risk

If bipolar disorder is a typical guest in your family tree, you might wonder about your own risk or that of your children. First, breathe—having a family history increases risk, it'sit's not destiIt'sIt's more about awareness and management. If you know there's a history of bipolar disorder in your family, you can be vigilant about the signs and symptoms. Early intervention is critical in managing bipolar disorder effectively, and being aware of the risk can help you and your healthcare provider make informed decisions about your mental health.

For those with a family history, consider regular mental health check-ups. Think of them like tune-ups for your mind. They provide a space to discuss any potential symptoms or concerns early on, similar to how you might manage a risk for diabetes or heart disease. Educating yourself and your family about the disorder also demystifies it and can prepare everyone to handle it better if it does show up.

Understanding the roles of genetics and environment in bipolar disorder does not just illuminate the pathways of risk and management; it empowers you to navigate these complex terrains with knowledge and proactive strategies. Whether tweaking lifestyle factors to manage stress better or engaging in therapy to unpack and mitigate potential triggers, you have the tools to influence how this interplay affects your life. So, keep this information close as you tailor your approach to living with or preventing bipolar disorder, making informed choices that enhance your well-being and resilience in the face of genetic and environmental challenges.

1.6 Understanding Mood Episodes: From Mania to Depression

Mania, in the realm of bipolar disorder isn't just about having a surplus of energy it's like riding a roller-coaster that only goes up. The signs of a manic episode can range from euphoria, excessive talking, and bursts of creative ideas to irritability, reckless decisions, and a diminished need for sleep. Imagine feeling so invincible that you decide to start five new business ventures in a week or impulsively book a flight to a country can't even pronounce—these aren't just quirky anecdotes; they are real-life manifestations of mania that can have serious, lasting consequences. This heightened state of activity and mood can lead to decisions that make sense at the moment but are disastrous in hindsight. The impact on behavior and decision-making is profound, affecting not only the individual but also their relationships and professional life. The fallout from these decisions can linger long after the manic episode subsides, often leaving a trail of personal and financial chaos.

Then, as if the body and mind tire from all that upward momentum, the inevitable crash into depression occurs. It isn't just sadness; this is a profound, pervasive low that can feel like all color has drained from the world. Bipolar depression differs from unipolar depression (the kind often experienced in major depressive disorder) in its relationship with manic episodes. In bipolar disorder, the depths of depression are usually more profound and more complex because they follow these extreme highs. The effects are debilitating: overwhelming feelings of hopelessness, a loss of interest in almost everything, and sometimes, thoughts of self-harm or suiciIt'sIt's a stark contrast to the occasionally exhilarating, frenzied highs of mania, and it can leave individuals feeling like they are living two different lives.

Mixed episodes, or mixed states, add another layer of complexity. Here, symptoms of mania and depression mix in a confusing cocktail. Imagine feeling energetically sad or despairingly impulsive—these paradoxical feelings can coexist in a mixed episode. This blending of highs and lows can make diagnosis and treatment particularly challenging. The mixed state is a turbulent weather system of emotion, where sun and storm clouds collide, leaving the individual unsure of which way the wind is blowing. These episodes are particularly risky, as the combination of depressive hopelessness and manic energy can increase the risk of suicide.

The cyclical nature of bipolar disorder, with its rotation of high, low, and sometimes mixed episodes, underscores the critical need for long-term management strategies. Recognizing the patterns in these cycles can be like learning to predict the weather—a skill that, while never perfect, can significantly mitigate the disorder's impact. Long-term management might include medication to stabilize mood, therapy to develop coping strategies, and lifestyle adjustments to promote stability. It also involves building a strong support network that can help during all weather conditions—the manic highs, the depressive lows, or the confusing mixed states.

Understanding these episodes in their entirety—recognizing their signs, symptoms, and the challenges they bring—is cruciIt'sIt's not just about weathering the storm; it's about preparing for it, knowing when it might arrive, and having the tools ready to ensure it causes as little disruption as possible. Recognizing early signs can often mean the difference between a minor disturbance and a major upheaval. In the world of bipolar disorder, knowledge and preparation are key. With the right strategies and supports in place, the roller-coaster can be less daunting and the weather less fearsome, allowing for a life that embraces all its seasons.

The Common Symptoms of Bipolar Depression

- Feelings of worthlessness or guilt
- Weight loss or gain (due to changes in how much you eat)
- Depressed mood most of the day
- Loss of interest in things you once enjoyed
- Trouble falling or staying asleep or sleeping too much
- Feeling irritated easily
- Fatigue or loss of energy
- Difficulty thinking, concentrating, and making decisions
- Thoughts of harming yourself

CHAPTER:2
THE INITIAL AFTERMATH:
COPING WITH DIAGNOSIS

Imagine you've just been handed a jigsaw puzzle, except the pieces aren't neatly boxed, and the picture you're supposed to assemble isn't on the lid—it's locked away in a vault. That's a bit of what it feels like to receive a bipolar diagnosis. Suddenly, you have all these pieces: symptoms, treatments, and advice, but none seem to fit together easily. Well, consider this chapter your guide to starting that puzzle, one piece at a time, with a dash of humor and a whole lot of understanding.

2.1 Just Diagnosed: Now What?

Initial Reactions

So, the doctor just dropped the B-word—Bipolar. You might feel like you've just been cast in a thriller, not necessarily one you auditioned for. It's OK. It's normal. It's expected. From the moment those words hit the air, you might feel a storm of emotions swirling inside—relief because finally, there's a name for the ride you've been on; fear because what does this label mean for your future; confusion because what even is bipolar disorder, really; or even denial, because surely, this must be a mistake.

These feelings? They don't just validate your experience; they are a universal ticket every person diagnosed with bipolar disorder holds. You're not alone in this cinema of chaos. Acknowledging these emotions is the first step towards managing them. It's like the opening scene of your personal epic—intense, yes, but essential for setting the stage for what comes next.

First Steps to Take

Now, onto the action plan. Think of it as your own movie montage—cutting between scenes of you gearing up to take control. First off, education is your armor. Understanding bipolar disorder robs it of some of its terror. Dive into reputable sources—books, medical journals, or trusted websites like the National Institute of Mental Health or the International Bipolar Foundation. Knowledge is power, and in your case, it's also strategy.

Next, assemble your crew. More than likely, your primary care provider or family doctor diagnosed you and will now refer you to a specialist for evaluation and treatment. A psychiatrist isn't just a doctor; they're more like a guide through this new terrain you're navigating. They can help customize your treatment plan, including medication, therapy, or both. A psychologist may be better suited for therapy, but you need a psychiatrist to prescribe medication. This step is about crafting your sword tailored to your battle. Sometimes, we carry around a little more emotional and mental baggage. This baggage can be more detrimental to someone with Bipolar because not only do you have to manage the illness but also deal with the lurking skeletons in the proverbial closet.

The Importance of Support

As you gear up for this journey, remember that every hero needs a fellowship—think Frodo and his gang. It's time to rally your support system. This crew can be family, friends, or even others who've been diagnosed with bipolar disorder. There's also immense strength in connecting with bipolar support groups, where you can share your experiences and learn from others who are walking similar paths These people aren't just your supporters, allies, confidantes, and cheerleaders. They're the ones who will see you through the plot twists and cliffhangers.

Self-Care Practices

Finally, let's talk about your daily training regimen—self-care. These aren't just spa days and smoothies (though those are nice!) It's about constructing a routine that includes regular sleep, balanced nutrition, physical activity, and, yes, mental breaks. Start simple. Maybe it's setting a bedtime, finding time for a walk, or carving out moments for meditation or journaling. Consider these the daily drills that keep you in shape for the main event—managing bipolar disorder. Establishing a routine will better help you track mood changes or potential triggers. If you are like me, you will resist therapy, exercising, and good eating habits—heck, I didn't do it before Bipolar; what makes anyone think I'll part with Haagen Dazs now?!

My path started in the basement of rock bottom. In a mild depression, around the end of 2020, the depression got progressively worse for the following year. Yes, a year. But I can't put it all at the feet of my diagnosis. I was injured at work and had to resign from an enjoyable job. Other plans fell apart one by one, including all attempts at finding a new job. Savings were dwindling, bills were mounting, and all my poor husband could do was watch me implode. Then, of course, the little things in life would not be left behind, so the toilet would back up, the car would drop the transmission, and the cat would decide to do its business in the middle of the kitchen. I mean, really?!

I finally started walking 10-15 minutes daily on the treadmill, sometimes with tears in my eyes, and noticed it made me feel better, so I kept it up for a while. Slowly, I worked for up to 45 minutes and then got bored. I couldn't forget the good feelings I got out of exercising, so I went to the internet to see what I could find. I had played with Pinterest for Christmas decorations a while back, so I started exploring the site further. I found many interesting things, and handmade journals caught my eye. Mind you, I didn't (still don't) believe I had an artistic gene in me. I could not draw a straight line with a ruler. You can find almost anything on Pinterest. I started noticing quotes and funny memes, and it felt less toxic than Facebook, so I started writing in the journals, and wow! I had so much to say, even if, especially, because no one would ever read these.

Reflective Pause

Take a moment here. Reflect on these initial steps. They're your foundation, your starting blocks. Each one is a move towards understanding, managing, and thriving with bipolar disorder. Write down one action you can take today from each of these steps. It could be as simple as bookmarking a medical site, calling a friend, or deciding tonight's bedtime. Small steps, significant strides.

2.2 Managing the Emotional Roller-coaster Post-Diagnosis

So, you've received your diagnosis, and suddenly, you're on this emotional see-saw, right? One minute you're up, the next you're down, and sometimes you're just hanging upside down, wondering which way is up. Managing these swings is like being the conductor of your emotional symphony—sometimes the music is harmonious, and other times, it's just cacophony. Let's talk about how to turn that chaos into a melody, starting with some solid emotional regulation techniques.

Mindfulness and cognitive behavioral strategies are your instruments here. I was hoping you wouldn't roll your eyes; although I have tried some of these, they are not mantras, incense, oils, or crystals. Think of mindfulness as your metronome, helping you keep pace with your thoughts and feelings without getting swept away. It's about sitting with your emotions and observing them like clouds passing in the sky—noticeable but not necessarily impactful. You can practice this through simple daily meditations or even mindful walking. Focus on being present, feeling each step and breath, and letting those intrusive thoughts stroll by. Look around and breathe with intent. Cognitive Behavioral Therapy (CBT), on the other hand, is like tuning your instrument. It helps you challenge and change those distorted thoughts and behaviors that throw you off-key. For instance, if you find yourself thinking, "This diagnosis means my life is over," CBT techniques teach you to reframe those thoughts to something more balanced and accurate, like, "This diagnosis is a challenge, but I can manage it with the right strategies."

Now, let's talk about navigating the fog of uncertainty that comes post-diagnosis. It's perfectly normal to feel like you're treading water in the ocean of "What ifs?" What if I can't manage this? What if it changes how people see me? Here's where building a mindset geared towards resilience and hope comes into play. Start by setting small, achievable goals each day. This could be anything from reading one chapter of a book on bipolar disorder to going for a 10-minute walk. Each small victory is a lighthouse guiding you through the mist, showing you that you can manage this, one step at a time. Also, keep a gratitude journal. I can tell you my journals were NOT about being grateful. They were dark, bitter, and full of barbs, giving the universe the finger most of the time. There were everyday challenges to write down three things I was grateful for. On more harrowing days, these notes were powerful reminders of the good still around me and how I climbed the previous rungs in the ladder.

Therapy can often be daunting, but think of it as finding a co-navigator for your journey through uncharted waters. A therapist specializing in bipolar disorder isn't just a clinician; they're a confidant, a strategist, and sometimes, a lifeline. In therapy, you have a safe space to unpack all the baggage you've been carrying. You can explore your feelings about the diagnosis, dissect your fears, and construct coping strategies in a structured environment. It's not about getting advice but about gaining clarity and tools to help you adjust your sails as you navigate these new seas.

Finally, let's consider the process of building a new normal. This isn't about returning to who you were before the diagnosis; it's about creating a life that acknowledges and accommodates your new reality. Start by integrating your treatment plan into your daily routine. Make your medication schedule as routine as your morning coffee. Build check-ins that match your mood as regularly as your nightly TV show binge. Then, slowly weave your personal goals and interests back into your life. Love painting? Set up a small studio corner in your home where you can dive into colors when you feel up to it. Passionate about writing? Start a blog about your journey with bipolar disorder. This new normal might look different but can still be uniquely and wonderfully yours. It's about creating a harmonious symphony, where bipolar disorder has a note, but it's not the entire melody.

2.3 Telling Your Loved Ones: Strategies and Tips

So, you've got this new piece of information about yourself— bipolar disorder. It's like suddenly finding out you're part secret agent, part mystery novel protagonist. Now comes one of the trickier parts of the plot: sharing this news with your loved ones. Deciding when and whom to tell about your diagnosis can feel like choosing the right moment to drop a plot twist in a story. It's essential, and timing is everything. You might want to consider telling those closest to you first or those who you think will provide the support you need. It's like casting characters for a pivotal scene. You wouldn't want someone who'll overreact or underreact in a crucial moment. Consider their personalities, the quality of your relationship, and their capacity to offer support.

When you're ready to share, picking a calm, private setting to talk without interruptions is vital. This isn't a conversation to have in the middle of a family barbecue or via text message. You want space where emotions can be expressed, and questions can be asked freely. Be prepared for a range of reactions. Some might take it in stride; others might be confused or upset. Remember, their first reactions aren't their final word—they're the beginning of a conversation. Just as you had time to adjust to your diagnosis, they'll need time, too.

Explaining bipolar disorder in clear, simple terms can help demystify your condition. Avoid medical jargon. Instead, try comparing it to something more relatable. You could say, "Imagine your brain is like a car, and most people's brains have reliable brakes and steady acceleration. My brain's features are a bit more unpredictable, which can make my moods and energy levels very high or very low. Treatment is like regular maintenance that helps keep the car—and me—running smoothly." Emphasize that bipolar disorder is manageable with treatment and that you're learning more about how to handle it every day. This helps frame your condition in a context that's not just about challenges but also solutions and management. Your loved ones may already have known "something was up," and it's a matter of including them in your new goals.

As you navigate through their reactions, prepare yourself for a mix of support and misunderstanding. Some might offer help immediately; others might pull away, unsure what to say or do. Some might even deny that you have a disorder at all. It's natural for people to react based on their perceptions of mental health, which are shaped by personal beliefs, stigma, and misinformation. If you encounter a reaction rooted in stigma or myth, use it as an opportunity to educate. You could say, "I know some people think that bipolar disorder means I'm unstable, but it's more like having a condition that I can manage with medication and therapy, much like diabetes."

Finally, embracing the support from your loved ones while setting necessary boundaries is crucial. Let them know precisely how they can help you. Maybe you need them to be more patient during your low phases, or perhaps you need them to listen without trying to fix things. At the same time, it's" OK to set boundaries around your mental health. If specific topics or comments make you uncomfortable, it's OK to say, "I appreciate your concern, but I'm not comfortable discussing that right now." This helps establish a supportive dialogue that respects your needs and boundaries.

Telling your loved ones about your bipolar diagnosis isn't just about sharing a part of your life; it's about inviting them to support you in a meaningful, informed way. It strengthens connections, dispels myths, and builds a network of support that will be invaluable as you manage your bipolar disorder. It's about letting them walk with you, equipped with understanding and compassion, as you navigate this part of your life. Remember, you're not handing them a burden; you're offering them a chance to be there for you, just as you would be for them.

2.4 Building Your Bipolar Management Toolkit

Imagine you're setting up a workshop. This isn't just any workshop—it's one where you craft your well-being, and each tool you add is customized to help manage your bipolar disorder effectively. Think of this as assembling your mental health toolkit, a collection of practical resources designed to keep the machine running smoothly, even during those unpredictable moments.

Essential Tools and Resources

First, let's talk about gadgets and gizmos—a.k.a. tools and apps—that can make managing bipolar disorder a bit like having a high-tech assistant on your side. A mood tracker is your go-to tool.

Apps like Daylio or eMoods allow you to log your daily mood swings, sleep patterns, and medication adherence. These apps are like having a personal mood diary in your pocket, providing insights and patterns you might miss in the daily hustle. Over time, you'll see trends to help you and your healthcare provider make informed decisions about your treatment plan.

Then there are educational websites, which serve as your encyclopedia. Websites like Psych Central or the Depression and Bipolar Support Alliance offer a wealth of articles, webinars, and forums where you can learn more about bipolar disorder and connect with others who share similar experiences. These resources are like chapters in a guidebook, offering new strategies, scientific updates, and personal stories that can illuminate different aspects of living with bipolar disorder.

Creating a Treatment Plan

Now, let's sketch out your blueprint—a personalized treatment plan. This isn't something you whip up in an afternoon. It's a detailed, thought-out plan created with your healthcare provider. Think of it as a recipe where the ingredients include your medication, therapy sessions, lifestyle adjustments, and any other interventions that suit your needs. The key here is customization. What works for one person might not work for another, so your treatment plan must reflect your unique situation, symptoms, and goals.

This plan should also be flexible. Just as a pilot adjusts a flight path due to weather changes, be prepared to tweak your treatment plan as you go along. This might mean adjusting dosages, trying new therapies, or shifting focus from one area to another based on how you respond to different treatments. Regular check-ins with your doctor are like those strategic meetings where you review what's working and what's not, ensuring that every element of the plan contributes effectively to your stability.

Emergency Planning

No matter how well you maintain your car, sometimes, you might still find yourself with a flat tire. That's why you need an emergency kit. In the context of bipolar management, this includes having a crisis plan in place. This plan should include contact information for your healthcare provider, a trusted friend or family member, and a local or national crisis hotline like the National Suicide Prevention Lifeline. Keep this information easily accessible—maybe in your wallet, on your fridge, or saved prominently on your phone. Just knowing it's there can provide a sense of security.

Additionally, inform a few trusted individuals about your emergency plan. These people can step in if you cannot manage on your own. They should know how to recognize the signs you're struggling with and clearly understand how they can best support you—whether helping you contact your doctor, staying with you until help arrives, or just being there to listen.

Lifestyle Adjustments for Stability

Lastly, let's fine-tune the machine by making lifestyle adjustments that promote stability. Sleep hygiene is your foundation. Try to stick to a regular sleep schedule, as sleep disruptions can trigger mood episodes. Create a bedtime routine that signals to your body it's time to wind down, perhaps by reading or meditating before bed.

Your diet also plays a role in your mental health. Foods rich in omega-3 fatty acids, like salmon and flaxseeds, can be beneficial, while a balanced diet helps stabilize your energy levels throughout the day. Regular physical activity is equally important. Exercise isn't just good for your body; it's a natural mood stabilizer. Even something as simple as a daily walk can significantly affect how you feel.

Incorporating these tools into your daily life creates a structured environment that supports your mental health. This doesn't mean rigidity; it's about creating a flexible framework that adjusts as your needs change. By building and continually updating your bipolar management toolkit, you're equipped not just to cope with bipolar disorder but to thrive despite it.

2.5 Seeking Professional Help: Finding the Right Team for You

When it comes to managing bipolar disorder, think of yourself as the director of a blockbuster movie. You've got a vision (your health goals) and a script (your treatment plan), but you need a stellar cast and crew to bring it all to life. This is where finding the right healthcare providers comes into play. Imagine you're casting for the critical roles in your support system movie. You wouldn't just pick any actor off the street, right? You want the Meryl Streep and Tom Hanks of healthcare—professionals who know their lines and can deliver them with empathy and expertise.

First up, your lead actors are the psychiatrist and psychologist. A psychiatrist is like the director of photography, helping to set the mood right with the appropriate treatment modalities, medication, or other medical interventions. When choosing a psychiatrist, look for someone with a track record in treating bipolar disorder. Their experience in navigating the complex landscape of mood disorders can make a significant difference in your treatment effectiveness. On the other hand, a psychologist, like a scriptwriter, delves deep into your experiences, helping you rewrite narratives that might not be serving you well anymore. They specialize in therapy to help you understand and manage how you think, behave, and react.

But this isn't just a two-person show. The multidisciplinary approach includes a variety of healthcare professionals who each bring their unique skills to the stage. Depending on your plan and financial means, you might consider a nutritionist as your production designer, setting the scene with a mood-stabilizing diet, or a personal trainer like a stunt coordinator helping you build strength and resilience. Each professional plays a pivotal role, and together, they ensure that every aspect of your health is addressed, making the management of bipolar disorder more comprehensive and integrated.

As you assemble this award-winning cast, you must audition them thoroughly. Here are some key questions to ask: What's your experience with bipolar disorder? How do you approach treatment? Can you outline how you'd customize my care? What's your policy on communication between sessions? These questions can help gauge whether their approach aligns with your needs and expectations, ensuring the professional relationship is comfortable and beneficial.

Navigating insurance and costs in healthcare can often feel like trying to understand tax law when all you did was a weekend course on personal finance. It's complex and, sometimes, downright frustrating. Start by understanding your insurance coverage. What does it cover? Are your preferred providers and treatments covered? If the jargon gets too much, customer service is your go-to. Remember, no question is too small regarding your health and finances.

For those navigating these waters without insurance, consider looking into sliding scale fee structures offered by many therapists, which adjust the cost based on your income. Community clinics and training institutions often provide services at a lower cost as part of their training programs. Additionally, online platforms can offer more affordable therapy options; some even provide subscriptions that make frequent sessions more economically feasible.

Building your healthcare team is about creating a circle of trust and expertise around you. Each member, from psychiatrist to therapist, from nutritionist to yoga instructor, plays a critical role in your well-being. Like in any good movie, every role is crucial, and how well the cast performs together can turn a good story into a great one. So take your time, choose wisely, and build a team that turns your health journey into a masterpiece.

2.6 Setting Realistic Goals and Expectations

After receiving a bipolar diagnosis, it can feel like you're suddenly supposed to become the CEO of a company called My Bipolar Life Inc. overnight. And like any good CEO, you need a strategic plan, right? Well, that's where setting realistic, achievable goals comes into play. It's not about plotting out your entire life trajectory in one evening but instead establishing manageable, bite-sized goals that steer you toward wellness and stability. Think of it as setting waypoints on a map to your preferred destination, knowing that you might sometimes take a scenic route or hit an unexpected detour.

Setting goals post-diagnosis is crucial because it gives you something concrete to work towards amidst the often overwhelming sea of information and emotions. These goals can be as simple as taking your medication at the same time every day, attending all scheduled therapy sessions for the month, or even just dedicating fifteen minutes a day to a relaxing activity like reading or meditation. The key here is flexibility—life with bipolar disorder is often unpredictable, and your goals need to be adaptable enough to accommodate the ebbs and flows of your condition. This flexibility helps reduce frustration and discouragement since you're not rigidly bound to a set of expectations that might not always align with the realities of living with bipolar disorder.

Now, let's talk about adjusting those expectations. It's easy to fall into the trap of idealizing treatment outcomes or expecting linear progress without setbacks. However, the nature of bipolar disorder means that the path to stability often includes some degree of trial and error, whether in finding the proper medication, the most effective therapeutic approaches, or the ideal lifestyle adjustments. Emphasizing progress over perfection allows you to celebrate the small victories along the way—a crucial component in building momentum and maintaining motivation. For instance, if you've managed to keep your appointments and stick to your medication schedule, that's a win, even if you still have bad days.

Celebrating milestones, no matter how small, reinforces a positive feedback loop. Did you endure a tough week without canceling a single therapy session? That's a milestone. Have you communicated your feelings during a mood swing more effectively than before? Another milestone. These celebrations can be simple acknowledgments or small rewards, like treating yourself to a movie night. They remind you of your progress and resilience, which are essential for fostering hope and motivation. They are the proof that despite the ups and downs, you are moving forward, one foot in front of the other.

Looking at the long-term outlook, it's logical to acknowledge that while bipolar disorder is a lifelong condition, it is also one that can be managed effectively with the proper treatment and strategies. Many people with bipolar disorder lead rich, fulfilling lives marked by successful careers, rewarding relationships, and vibrant social lives. The key lies in ongoing management, which includes consistent medication adherence, regular therapy, and a stable support system. This doesn't mean there won't be challenging days or even relapses. However, with each challenge comes an opportunity to learn more about managing the condition, refining your strategies, and continuing to evolve your approach to living with bipolar disorder.

Remember to be kind to yourself when setting goals and expectations for your life post-diagnosis. You are learning to navigate a new aspect of your life that requires patience, perseverance, and self-compassion. Each step forward, no matter how small, is a piece of the puzzle fitting into place, gradually revealing a picture of a life not defined by bipolar disorder but enhanced by the depth, resilience, and understanding it brings.

As this chapter closes, we've equipped ourselves with realistic goals, adjusted our expectations, and prepared to celebrate every small victory on the path to managing bipolar disorder. These strategies are not just about coping; they're about thriving. They remind us that each step forward enriches our journey, offering valuable lessons and deeper insights into both the challenges and triumphs of living with bipolar disorder. With these tools in hand, we turn the page, ready to explore deeper into the practicalities and personal adjustments that make navigating this path not only possible but also profoundly rewarding.

CHAPTER:3
PSYCHIATRIC MEDS 101

This chapter aims to dispel common misconceptions surrounding psychiatric medications. While some individuals harbor reservations about medication use, others, like myself, rely on them for daily functioning. Dismissing the effectiveness of drugs as not being 'real' is unfounded. Medications offer respite to the brain from operating under abnormal conditions. There is skepticism toward pharmaceutical companies due to misleading marketing or a lack of transparency regarding a product's efficacy. Additionally, there is debate over symptom management versus disease eradication and whether specific side effects that do not go away are worth the discomfort.

3.1 Understanding Psychiatric Medications

Understanding how these medications work is like unraveling the mystery behind a magic trick. It's about making the complex simple. For instance, mood stabilizers ensure optimal communication between nerves in the brain, just like tuning an instrument to achieve perfect harmony. Antipsychotics dampen or block the effects of dopamine, a neurotransmitter often excessively active during manic episodes. It's akin to lowering the volume when the music becomes overwhelming, preventing the brain from becoming inundated. Antidepressants elevate serotonin and norepinephrine levels in the brain to enhance mood, analogous to adding sugar to coffee to sweeten it. Mood stabilizers are commonly used to manage conditions like bipolar disorder by preventing extreme highs (mania) and lows (depression). These medications regulate certain chemicals in the brain, such as neurotransmitters, which play a role in controlling mood.

The key to successful medication use is not just about taking the medication; it's about finding the correct prescription and dosage. This often involves a trial-and-error process, which can be challenging. However, it's important to remember that it's a collaborative effort between you and your doctor. Clear communication is crucial to achieve the perfect biochemical equilibrium. You shouldn't feel drugged when you find the right combination; you should feel more like your usual self. These medications will not change who you are. This collaborative approach reassures you that you are not alone in this journey.

3.2 Navigating Side Effects

Vigilance is crucial when it comes to side effects. These can range from minor inconveniences to significant concerns necessitating dosage adjustments or medication changes. It is recommended you read the literature on your particular prescription. Ensure your doctor knows all medications you're taking to mitigate interactions and minimize side effects. Many medications have been around since the mid-1950s, and their effects and side effects have been well-documented. These are referred to as 'typical' or first-generation medications. In the 90s, new medications were developed and are referred to as second-generation or 'atypical' medications. A common concern among antipsychotic medications is Tardive Dyskinesia (TD), which causes involuntary muscle movements. This can be controlled with an additional pill or by reducing dosage. Being proactive about side effects can help you manage your health more effectively.

One last caution on side effects: Like many other things in our bodies, these medications are metabolized by the liver or the kidneys; therefore, it is wise to have your doctor monitor both liver and kidney functions as necessary.

3.3 Understanding Medication Options

Numerous resources offer guidance through the plethora of medication options. Don't be daunted by terms like antipsychotics, anticonvulsants, reuptake inhibitors, or all the acronyms; many medications target multiple areas of the brain and neurotransmitter chemicals. Our understanding of how some medications work is limited, reflecting the vast gaps in our knowledge of the brain. Only recently have we been able to measure the levels of neurotransmitters in the brain to some extent. With just that bit of progress, we have been able to determine that the term 'chemical imbalance' is a misnomer because, in fact, there is no noticeable reduction of serotonin in depression. However, the term helps clarify and visualize the reason for the disease.

Another example of unintentional effects of drugs is that some diabetes management medications are now being used on non-diabetics for weight loss. Once the effects are observed, the medication goes through a process to see if it can be approved for the alternate treatment. Discussing how the brain works may help you further navigate this maze. However, it is a little far from the scope of this book because I promised no overtechnical medical jargon. But I can refer you to Ashley L. Peterson's "Psych Meds Made Simple." She does a beautiful job explaining neurotransmitters, receptors, regions of the brain, and what they have to do with our illnesses.

To give a general idea, below is a list of some of the naturally occurring chemicals in humans:

- **Serotonin**: Regulates mood, appetite, sleep, and memory. Imbalances in serotonin levels are associated with mood disorders like depression and anxiety.

- **Dopamine**: Plays a role in motivation, pleasure, reward, and movement control. It is involved in addiction, attention, and mood regulation.

- **Epinephrine (adrenaline)**: A neurotransmitter and stress hormone that plays a role in attention, alertness, and the body's fight-or-flight response.

- **Acetylcholine**: Involved in muscle movement, learning, memory, and attention and in regulating the autonomic nervous system.

- **Gamma-aminobutyric acid (GABA)**: An inhibitory neurotransmitter that helps reduce neuronal excitability. It is involved in relaxation, sleep, and anxiety regulation.

- **Glutamate**: Functions as the primary excitatory neurotransmitter in the brain, playing a role in learning, memory, and synaptic plasticity.

- **Endorphins**: Act as natural painkillers and are involved in the body's response to stress and exercise. They also contribute to feelings of pleasure and euphoria.

3.4 Addressing Common Misconceptions

One common misconception is that psychiatric medications are a crutch for the weak or that they fundamentally alter who you are. This stigma can prevent people from seeking the help they need. It's necessary to recognize that mental health conditions are as real and as debilitating as physical illnesses. Just as you wouldn't tell someone with diabetes to forgo insulin, it's unreasonable to suggest that someone with a mental health disorder should avoid medication. These medications do not change your personality or who you are; they help you manage your condition so you can be yourself.

Another myth is that medications are a quick fix. In reality, finding the proper medication and dosage is often a lengthy process involving careful monitoring and adjustments. This trial-and-error approach can be frustrating, but it's essential for finding the most effective treatment with the fewest side effects. Patience, persistence, and open communication with your healthcare provider are key to successful treatment.

There's also a belief that natural or holistic remedies are always better than pharmaceuticals. While lifestyle changes, therapy, and holistic approaches can be beneficial, they are not always sufficient on their own. Medications can play a crucial role in managing symptoms that other treatments might not fully address. It's not a matter of choosing one over the other but finding a balanced approach that works for you.

In conclusion, psychiatric medications are an essential tool in the treatment of mental health disorders. They help restore balance to the brain's chemistry, enabling individuals to lead more stable and fulfilling lives. Misconceptions about these medications can prevent people from seeking the help they need but understanding how they work and the role they play in managing mental health can dispel these myths. Remember, the journey to finding the correct medication is a collaborative effort between you and your doctor, and it's a process that requires patience, vigilance, and open communication. By being informed and proactive about your treatment, you can take control of your mental health and improve your quality of life.

3.5 Newer Treatment Modalities

Recent advancements in psychiatric treatment are expanding beyond traditional medications:

- **Third-Generation Antipsychotics**: Drugs like aripiprazole (Abilify) and brexpiprazole (Rexulti) offer different mechanisms of action and improved side effect profiles compared to earlier antipsychotics.

- **Long-Acting Injectables (LAIs)**: These are used for conditions like schizophrenia and bipolar disorder, providing medication that lasts for weeks or months, improving adherence and outcomes.

- **Ketamine and Esketamine**: These newer treatments for depression work rapidly, within hours or days, unlike traditional antidepressants that can take weeks to become effective. Esketamine, delivered as a nasal spray, has been particularly promising for treatment-resistant depression.

3.6 Pharmacogenomics

Pharmacogenomics is an emerging field that studies how an individual's genetic makeup affects their drug response. This has significant implications for psychiatric medications:

- **Personalized Medicine**: By analyzing a patient's genetic profile, doctors can better predict which medications and dosages will be most effective and have the fewest side effects. This personalized approach reduces the trial-and-error process of finding the proper medication.

3.7 Non-Traditional Medications

Some medications not traditionally used for psychiatric conditions are finding new roles in mental health treatment:

- **Antihypertensives**: Drugs like propranolol, a beta-blocker, are used off-label to manage anxiety and PTSD symptoms due to their effects on physical anxiety symptoms.

- **Anticonvulsants**: Medications like lamotrigine and valproate, initially developed for epilepsy, are now commonly used as mood stabilizers in bipolar disorder.

3.8 Off-Label Use

Off-label use of medications is common in psychiatry. This refers to prescribing drugs for conditions outside their approved indications:

- **Examples**: Clonidine, approved for hypertension, is often used to treat ADHD and anxiety. Similarly, antipsychotics like quetiapine are sometimes used off-label for insomnia due to their sedative properties.

The Future of Psychiatric Medications

Looking ahead, the future of psychiatric medications holds promise with ongoing research and development:

- **Neurostimulation**: Techniques like transcranial magnetic stimulation (TMS) and deep brain stimulation (DBS) are being explored as alternatives or adjuncts to medication for treatment-resistant conditions.

- **New Mechanisms**: Research into new neurotransmitter systems and pathways is ongoing, potentially leading to novel medications with unique mechanisms of action and better side effect profiles.

CHAPTER:4
TREATMENT STRATEGIES AND MANAGEMENT

Welcome to the wild world of managing bipolar disorder, where the right combination of tools, tricks, and treatments can sometimes feel like you're trying to solve a Rubik's Cube blindfolded. But fear not! This chapter is about demystifying one of the most crucial aspects of that puzzle: medications. Think of it as your guide to the pharmacy aisle, except instead of finding the best deal on shampoo, you're navigating through mood stabilizers, antipsychotics, and antidepressants. Exciting, right? Let's dive in without tripping over medical jargon and maybe even have a few laughs.

4.1 Understanding Medication Options

Navigating the medication tangle in bipolar disorder can be a bit like finding your way through a carnival funhouse—distorted mirrors and all. Several medications are commonly prescribed, each playing a different role in balancing the brain's biochemistry. First up, we have mood stabilizers. These are the heavy lifters, helping to even out the highs of mania and the lows of depression. Think of them as your emotional shock absorbers, smoothing those bumpy neurological roads.

Next, we introduce the antipsychotics. Despite their somewhat intimidating name, these medications are like the bouncers at the club of your brain. They help manage severe symptoms of mania and also help with psychotic symptoms, which can include delusions or hallucinations, should those be part of your experience.

Last but not least, we have antidepressants. Typically used cautiously in bipolar disorder due to the risk of triggering manic episodes, they're like the person who brings you a hot cup of tea (or a strong coffee) when you're feeling down, helping lift the fog of depression.

Navigating this medley of medications isn't about popping pills willy-nilly but finding a tailored blend that works for your unique brain chemistry. It's a bit like being a DJ mixing tracks—you need to find the right balance so the beat goes on smoothly without any unexpected drops. We will cover more about medications in the next chapter.

Medication Adherence

Sticking to your medication plan is as crucial as the plan itself. But let's be honest; adding one more thing to your daily to-do list isn't always easy. Here's where strategies to keep you on track come in handy. Setting reminders on your phone, using a pill organizer, or aligning your medication times with daily routines like brushing your teeth can all help make adherence less of a chore. It's about weaving these habits into the fabric of your day until they become as automatic as checking your email.

Medication adherence is critical for the success of psychiatric treatment:

Challenges: Patients may struggle with adherence due to side effects, forgetfulness, or misunderstanding the importance of taking their medication consistently.

Strategies: Using pill organizers, setting reminders, and simplifying dosing schedules can help improve adherence. Long-acting injectables can also ensure consistent medication levels.

Remember, these medications are not just pills but pillars that support your mental architecture. Missing doses or stopping suddenly can not only diminish their effectiveness but also lead to withdrawal symptoms or relapse. It's like skipping a beat in a meticulously timed dance routine—it throws everything off.

Collaborating with Your Doctor

Lastly, let's talk about perfecting the art of collaboration with your doctor. Open communication about how the medication affects you, any side effects you're experiencing, and your concerns make a huge difference. It's like having a co-pilot in the cockpit; you're on the journey together, navigating through the clouds. Don't hesitate to ask questions or express concerns—your health, mind, and life are on the line.

Sharing detailed feedback with your doctor helps you tailor your treatment plan more effectively. Maybe a particular medication makes you feel too tired, or another isn't entirely taking the edge off depression. This feedback is invaluable. It helps your doctor adjust dosages or try new medications, ensuring that your treatment plan fits not just a diagnosis but you as an individual.

Navigating the world of medications for bipolar disorder is an indispensable element of your overall management strategy. It's about more than just swallowing pills; it's about understanding their role, sticking to your regimen, and working collaboratively with your healthcare provider to fine-tune your treatment. Whether you're a newbie just starting this journey or a seasoned traveler on the bipolar road, getting the medication mix right can make all the difference. So, take charge, stay informed, and open the lines of communication with your doctor. Your brain will thank you.

4.2 Psychotherapy and Bipolar: A Guide to Effective Therapy Options

When it comes to navigating the ups and downs of bipolar disorder, psychotherapy is like having a skilled navigator aboard your ship, helping you steer through stormy seas and sunny days alike. It's not just about talking; it's about transforming your approach to daily challenges, giving you the tools to manage your mood swings and maintain relationships. Let's break down the types of psychotherapy that often stand out in the treatment of bipolar disorder, each with its unique flavor and strengths.

Cognitive Behavioral Therapy (CBT) is like having a mental detective by your side, helping you to spot and change thought patterns that may lead you to emotional pitfalls. Focuses on changing unhelpful thought patterns and behaviors through cognitive restructuring and skill development. Think of it as mental judo; you learn to leverage your thoughts in a way that helps you balance your mental state. It's convenient for tackling the negative thought spirals that can occur during depressive episodes or the unchecked optimism of manic phases. By recognizing these thoughts as symptoms of your disorder rather than truths, you can start to take control back from bipolar disorder's grip.

Dialectical Behavior Therapy (DBT), on the other hand, emphasizes navigating emotional storms by teaching you to balance acceptance and change. It integrates mindfulness (being fully present in the moment), distress tolerance (getting through tough times without making them worse), emotional regulation (managing and responding to intense feelings effectively), and interpersonal effectiveness to help individuals manage intense emotions and improve relationships. Initially developed for borderline personality disorder, its usefulness in controlling the fierce emotional swings in bipolar disorder has gained recognition.

Family-focused therapy brings your support crew into the fold, training them alongside you in the skills needed to manage bipolar disorder. It's about strengthening your support network by giving your loved ones the tools and understanding necessary to assist you. They learn about warning signs and the best response methods, which can make all the difference during a crisis or instability. Think of it as fortifying your home's foundations, ensuring everyone inside knows how to keep it stable.

Integrating therapy with medication creates a synergy that often leads to better outcomes. Imagine you are trying to cultivate a beautiful garden—medication helps to keep the weeds at bay while therapy nurtures the growth of healthy plants. Together, they ensure a more resilient and flourishing garden. Medication can stabilize your mood swings, making it easier to engage in therapy, while the skills and insights gained from therapy can help you make the most of your medication by sticking to your treatment plan and avoiding triggers that could lead to mood episodes.

Finding the right therapist is significant; it's like finding the right personal trainer for your mental health. You need someone who isn't just qualified but also someone you can click with, someone who gets it. Start by looking for therapists who specialize in bipolar disorder or mood disorders more broadly. They're more likely to understand the nuances of the condition and offer the most effective strategies. When you first meet, don't hesitate to ask about their experience and approach. Questions like, "How do you tailor your therapy to work with bipolar disorder?" or "Can you tell me about your experiences with other clients who have bipolar disorder?" can provide insights into their expertise and approach.

Don't forget to use resources such as psychologytoday.com, where you can filter therapists by specialty and insurance. Local support groups and your psychiatrist may also have recommendations. Remember, finding the right therapist might take time. It's like dating; you might not find the perfect match on the first try, but finding someone who can genuinely support your journey to stability is worth the effort.

In sum, psychotherapy offers a toolkit for living with bipolar disorder, not just by managing symptoms but by enriching your understanding of yourself and enhancing your relationships. Whether through CBT (Cognitive Behavioral Therapy), DBT (Dialectical Behavior Therapy), family-focused therapy, or another modality, therapy can be a cornerstone of effective bipolar disorder management, providing structure, support, and strategies for a fulfilling life despite the challenges of the condition.

Lifestyle Management: Diet, Exercise, and Sleep

Imagine that your body is like a finely tuned sports car; what you put into it and how you treat it can dictate how well it performs. For those navigating the winding roads of bipolar disorder, understanding the profound impact of diet, exercise, and sleep on your overall health isn't just good advice—it's crucial maintenance.

Diet and Nutrition

Let's start with fuel—your diet. Food is not just sustenance; it's information for your body and brain, and the right kinds can help stabilize your mood and enhance your energy levels. Think of your gut as a second brain, intricately linked to your actual brain. When your gut is happy and stocked with good fuel, it sends positive signals to your brain, potentially leading to more stable moods. So, what's on the menu for keeping both brains happy?

A bipolar-friendly diet leans heavily on the Mediterranean eating style—rich in vegetables, fruits, whole grains, fish, and olive oil. These foods are not just delicious; they are also packed with nutrients that can help combat the biological stress that often accompanies bipolar disorder. Omega-3 fatty acids found abundantly in fish like salmon and flaxseeds are particularly good at this. They're like your brain's best friends, helping to smooth out mood swings and protect against depression. On the other hand, try to steer clear of the villains—highly processed foods, excessive caffeine, and sugar. These can lead to mood crashes and throw your energy levels out of whack.

Incorporating these dietary changes doesn't have to be a chore or a bore. Spice it up; make it an adventure! Experiment with new recipes that include these brain-boosting foods. Maybe start a weekly tradition of cooking a new dish from a different culture that follows these guidelines. Not only are you feeding your body what it needs, but you're also breaking the monotony that sometimes comes with dietary restrictions.

Exercise as a Tool

Next up, let's talk about exercise. If diet is your car's fuel, exercise is the maintenance that keeps it running smoothly. Regular physical activity is a fantastic tool for managing bipolar disorder. It helps regulate mood, reduce stress, and improve sleep—trifecta! When you exercise, your brain releases endorphins, sometimes known as feel-good hormones. It's like giving your brain a mini-vacation.

The key here is regularity and enjoyment. Find activities that you actually enjoy. Hate running? No problem. How about dancing, hiking, or maybe a cycling class? The goal is to get moving, whatever that looks like for you. Aim for moderate intensity, and try to be consistent. Setting small, achievable goals, like a 30-minute walk five days a week, can make a big difference. It's not about training for a marathon (unless that's your thing) but about weaving movement into your day to keep your mood balanced.

The Importance of Sleep

Let's dim the lights and talk about sleep—your body's best regeneration tool. Sleep and bipolar disorder have a complex relationship. Poor sleep can trigger manic episodes or deepen depressive episodes, while stable sleep patterns tend to support mood stability. Developing good sleep hygiene is crucial. This means creating a bedtime routine that signals to your body it's time to wind down. Maybe it's a warm bath, turning off blue light-emitting devices an hour before bed, or reading a book chapter (preferably not a thriller!).

Keep your sleep and wake times consistent, even on weekends. This regularity trains your brain when to shut down for rest and stabilizes your internal clock, which can help manage your mood. Consider it setting your body's alarm system to protect against mood swings.

Integrating Lifestyle Changes

Finally, let's piece it all together. Integrating these changes into your daily routine might seem daunting at first. Start small. Introduce changes gradually, and celebrate the small victories. Maybe this week, you focus on improving your diet; next week, you add a few exercise routines; and the week after, you tighten up your sleep schedule. Small steps lead to significant changes.

Remember, managing bipolar disorder is a holistic journey. Your diet, exercise, and sleep are not just parts of a treatment plan—they are integral components of a healthy lifestyle. Each element supports the other, creating a synergy that can significantly enhance your ability to manage your mood and improve your overall quality of life. So, take the time to nourish your body, challenge it with physical activity, and rest it well. Your mind will thank you, and you might find yourself feeling more balanced and prepared to handle whatever twists and turns bipolar disorder throws your way.

4.4 The Impact of Stress and How to Manage It

Let's face it: Stress is as avoidable as reruns of old sitcoms on TV—it's always there, and sometimes it's mildly entertaining, but often, it just feels repetitive and exhausting. For those navigating the waves of bipolar disorder, stress isn't just a nuisance; it can be a significant trigger, turning what feels like a manageable day into an emotional upheaval. Understanding how stress interacts with bipolar disorder isn't just about keeping your sanity on a bad day; it's about equipping yourself with tools to keep the boat steady even when the weather turns foul.

Stress, in the context of bipolar disorder, can act like a spark in a pile of dry leaves. It can ignite manic or depressive episodes, making it not just an emotional response but a biochemical game-changer. This happens because stress hormones like cortisol can affect brain function, influencing mood, thinking, and even how you process other stimuli. It's like turning up the volume on your emotions; everything feels more intense, and suddenly, the coping mechanisms you usually rely on might not cut it. This is why embedding effective stress management techniques into your daily routine isn't just good practice; it's essential maintenance for your mental health.

So, how do you keep stress from steering the ship? First, recognize what your stressors are. These can be as obvious as a significant life change or as subtle as a poor night's sleep. Sometimes, writing these down can help you see patterns or triggers you weren't aware of. Next, arm yourself with a toolbox of stress reduction techniques. Relaxation exercises can be a good start. This isn't just about taking deep breaths or meditating, though those are excellent strategies. It's also about finding activities that distract your mind from stressors and give you a break. Maybe it's painting, playing an instrument, or even gardening—anything that helps you shift gears and allows your brain a moment to rest and reset.

Time management strategies also play a crucial role. Often, stress bubbles up from feeling like you're running out of time or not in control of your schedule. By prioritizing tasks, setting realistic goals, and breaking down your day into manageable chunks, you can reduce the chaos that often leads to stress. Think of it as decluttering your day; when each task has its place, and you know what to expect, the day feels less overwhelming.

Setting healthy boundaries is another strategic move. This means learning to say no or step back when overwhelmed. It's about recognizing your limits and communicating them to others. In a world that often praises the hustle, stepping off the treadmill and catching your breath is okay. Remember, saying no to others sometimes means saying yes to your well-being.

Creating a supportive, low-stress environment is like setting the stage for a smoother performance. At home, this might mean organizing your space to reduce chaos, using soothing colors or decor, and establishing a sanctuary where you can retreat when things get too hectic. At work, it might involve negotiating your workload or deadlines to suit your mental health needs better or setting up your workspace to minimize stress. Think about what changes can make your daily environments more calming and supportive, and don't hesitate to make those changes.

Long-term stress management is about building resilience. It's not just about handling stress as it comes but developing systems and habits that make you less susceptible to stress in the first place. Regular exercise, a consistent sleep schedule, and ongoing therapy or support groups can all contribute to a baseline of stability that makes you less likely to be knocked off balance when stress does hit. It's about fortifying your defenses, not just patching up leaks as they happen.

Incorporating these strategies into your life doesn't just help manage stress; it transforms how you interact with your world. It's about turning stress management from a fire-fighting tool into a blueprint for a more balanced, resilient life. By understanding the triggers, employing reduction techniques, and creating supportive environments, you're not just surviving with bipolar disorder; you're thriving despite it.

4.5 Holistic Approaches: Complementing Traditional Treatments

When you think about managing bipolar disorder, your mind might first wander to the usual suspects: medications and therapy. But imagine adding some more tools to your wellness toolkit—ones that might seem a bit unconventional but can harmonize beautifully with your standard care. I'm talking about holistic approaches like acupuncture, yoga, and meditation. These aren't just new-age fads; they're practices rooted in ancient traditions, now backed by modern science and gaining ground as valuable allies in managing bipolar disorder.

Let's start with acupuncture, a technique involving the insertion of very thin needles through your skin at strategic points on your body, a key component of traditional Chinese medicine. It's like having a secret map of energy points on your body, and when these points are activated, they can help recalibrate your body's energy flow or Qi. For those with bipolar disorder, acupuncture has been noted to help reduce stress and anxiety, potentially lessening the intensity of mood swings. Picture this as trying to smooth out waves before they become too turbulent. While the thought of needles might make some a bit squeamish, many report these sessions as surprisingly relaxing and rejuvenating.

Then, there's yoga, which is much more than just stretching and holding poses. It's a complete package of benefits wrapped in calm and centeredness. Yoga combines physical postures, breathing exercises, and meditation to enhance physical flexibility, mental clarity, and emotional stability. For someone managing bipolar disorder, this trinity can be particularly potent. Engaging in yoga can be akin to tuning an instrument—aligning your body, mind, and emotions to play harmoniously. It's about building inner strength and flexibility, not just physically but also emotionally, providing a buffer against the strain of mood swings.

Meditation, the practice of mindfulness or focused thought, can be a profound tool for those with bipolar disorder. It's about sitting with your thoughts in a way that lets you observe them without becoming entangled. Over time, this practice can enhance your ability to monitor your mood and triggers more effectively, fostering a kind of mental agility that can be crucial in managing the disorder. Think of it as training your mind to be an observer, which can help you detach and assess rather than spiral in moments of high emotion or stress.

My personal favorite is Pilates. Pilates is a comprehensive fitness system with numerous benefits, including improved strength, flexibility, posture, and mental well-being. It's suitable for people of all ages and fitness levels and can be practiced in various settings, including gyms, studios, and even at home, with minimal equipment. It does not impact your joints, and focusing on breathing fully helps to center you.

While these practices offer promising benefits, it's crucial to incorporate them into your treatment plan with care and knowledge. Always consult with your healthcare provider before starting any new treatment regimen. They can help you integrate these holistic practices to support and enhance your treatment plan. For instance, combining meditation with medication might help you achieve better emotional balance, while yoga could complement therapy by reducing physical tension and mental stress that exacerbate symptoms.

Let's dive into some personal stories highlighting these holistic approaches' real-world impact. Consider Sarah, a long-time sufferer of bipolar II disorder, who found yoga not just a physical exercise but a lifeline. For her, yoga became a daily ritual that helped stabilize her mood and provided a sense of control over her body and mind. Then there's Mike, who explored acupuncture as an adjunct to his medication, only to discover that the sessions significantly reduced his anxiety, a common trigger for his depressive episodes. These stories underscore the potential of holistic practices to complement traditional treatments and enhance overall well-being.

Incorporating holistic approaches into your bipolar management strategy offers a broader canvas of options. It's about personalizing your treatment, mixing traditional and holistic tools to create a tailored approach that addresses your unique needs. Whether it's the calming flow of yoga, the centeredness of meditation, or the balancing touch of acupuncture or Pilates, each practice offers a pathway to greater harmony and health. Embrace these options with openness and curiosity, and you might find they add not only relief but also enrichment to your journey of managing bipolar disorder, painting a fuller picture of wellness that extends beyond conventional treatments.

4.6 Navigating Treatment Side Effects and Balance

When you first start your medication for bipolar disorder, it's like setting sail on a voyage across a vast ocean. The journey promises smoother seas, but sometimes, you must weather a few storms. Side effects from medications can be those storms—unpredictable and unsettling. Whether it's a queasy stomach from your mood stabilizers, a drowsy fog from your antipsychotics, or a case of the jitters from your antidepressants, side effects are often the crew members on your medication ship that you didn't realize you hired.

Common side effects can vary widely, but they often include nausea, weight gain, dizziness, or sleep disturbances. Imagine you're at a buffet where you're served a platter of unwanted side dishes instead of picking dishes that tantalize your taste buds. It's crucial not to push these around your plate but to find ways to manage them effectively. Simple strategies might involve adjusting the timing of when you take your meds—perhaps taking them with food to ease nausea or switching to evening doses to counter drowsiness. Sometimes, it's about adding a little something extra to your daily routine, like a morning walk or an additional glass of water, to counterbalance the side effects you're experiencing. Most of these side effects taper off after two weeks, others a little longer. I suffer from tremors. My solution was to step down the dosage of my mood stabilizer.

Knowing when to speak up about side effects is like knowing when to call in a lifeline during a game show. You don't have to struggle silently, guessing at solutions. Open communication with your healthcare provider is required. They're like your co-navigators; let them know what's going on. Many side effects can be managed with adjustments to your treatment plan, including tweaking dosages, switching medications, or adding remedies to counteract specific side effects. It's like adjusting your sails to the wind; sometimes, a slight shift can significantly affect how smoothly you sail.

Balancing the benefits of treatment with its side effects is a bit like being a judge at a talent show; you have to weigh the performances (benefits) against the stage mishaps (side effects). It's essential to consider how the treatment improves your quality of life. Is the mood stabilization worth the extra pounds? Does the clarity brought by antidepressants justify feeling a bit jittery? These are personal decisions; sometimes, they're tough calls. It's about looking at your life and deciding what's most important for your well-being. Remember, the goal of treatment is not just to reduce symptoms of bipolar disorder but to enhance your overall quality of life.

Empowering yourself to advocate in your treatment discussions is like stepping up to the captain's deck of your ship. You know the waters best. If something doesn't feel right or the side effects overshadow the benefits, it's your right and responsibility to speak up. Prepare for appointments with notes on what you've experienced, do your research, and don't be shy about asking for adjustments. It's about having a dialogue, not a monologue, with your healthcare provider. Make your voice heard, and ensure your treatment plan is a true collaboration tailored to your needs.

Navigating treatment side effects is an integral part of managing bipolar disorder. It requires awareness, communication, and, sometimes, a bit of creativity. By understanding common side effects, speaking up, balancing benefits with drawbacks, and advocating for yourself, you can find a treatment balance that manages your symptoms and supports a well-lived life. Remember, it's not just about weathering storms but about enjoying the journey, and with the right strategies, you can continue to steer towards clearer skies.

As we close this chapter on navigating treatment side effects, remember that the journey with bipolar disorder is both complex and manageable. Each step you take—adjusting medications, communicating with your doctor, or advocating for your needs—

builds a stronger foundation for your ongoing management. These strategies are crucial, not just for handling the challenges of today but for paving the way to a more stable and fulfilling tomorrow. As you continue to navigate these waters, know that each effort contributes to a broader journey towards wellness, one where balance isn't just possible but achievable. Stay the course, adjust as necessary, and keep your sights on the horizon of your best life. Now, let's sail onward to exploring further dimensions of living with bipolar disorder in the next chapter.

CHAPTER:5
DAILY LIFE ADJUSTMENTS AND COPING STRATEGIES

Have you ever felt like you're trying to juggle flaming torches while riding a unicycle on a tightrope? Well, managing daily life with bipolar disorder can sometimes feel a bit like that—exciting, unpredictable, and, yes, a tad overwhelming. But here's the good news: incorporating structured routines into your day can be like having a safety net below that tightrope, providing stability and confidence as you navigate your day. This chapter is about turning those flaming torches into manageable juggling balls and, perhaps, with some practice, making that unicycle ride a smooth sail.

5.1 Routine as a Rescue: Structuring Your Day for Stability

Benefits of a Routine

Imagine your daily routine as the rhythm section of a band—it might not always be the flashiest part, but boy, does it keep the music flowing smoothly! For those with bipolar disorder, a well-structured routine can be a lifesaver. It provides a predictable and familiar pattern that can help soothe the brain, reducing the likelihood of manic or depressive episodes. This doesn't just apply to big things like work or appointments; it includes little things like eating, exercising, or sleeping before bed.

Consistency is key. By waking up, taking medications, working, and sleeping regularly, you create a rhythm your body and mind can tune with. It's like setting the tempo for your daily life symphony—too fast, and the music gets chaotic, too slow, and drags. But just right? Harmony. This regularity helps regulate your body's internal clock, or circadian rhythm, which is crucial in managing mood swings. Think of it as teaching your body to expect what's next, which can be incredibly comforting in a world that often feels like it's spinning a little too fast.

Creating a Personalized Routine

But here's the twist: while routines are great, they aren't one-size-fits-all. Your routine must be tailored to fit your life, needs, and, yes, your quirks. Start by mapping out a typical day, noting the must-dos and the want-to-dos. Include time slots for non-negotiables, like taking medication or attending therapy sessions. Then, weave in activities that bring you joy or provide relaxation. Do you love to read? Set aside 30 minutes before bed as your designated reading time. Is coffee your morning ritual? Build that into your morning routine as something to savor, not just gulp down.

Use tools that help you stick to this routine. Apps that remind you to take your meds, calendars ping you about appointments, or even a good old-fashioned planner can help keep you on track. The goal is to build a routine that doesn't feel like a straitjacket but rather like your favorite cozy sweater—comforting, reliable, and snugly fitting into your life.

Flexibility Within Structure

However, life is nothing if not a series of unexpected events. While a routine provides structure, being too rigid can actually create stress, which is counterproductive. It's essential to build flexibility into your routine. For instance, if you've planned to go to the gym in the morning but wake up feeling sluggish and out of sorts, it might be better to adjust your schedule and go for a gentle walk in the evening instead.

Think of your routine as a guideline, not a rulebook. Life will throw curveballs—sick days, surprise visits, work crises—and your routine should be resilient enough to handle these. This flexibility reduces stress and empowers you to make choices that best suit your needs at any given moment, fostering a sense of control and self-efficacy.

Examples of Successful Routines

Let's draw some inspiration from others who've mastered the art of the routine. Take Julia, for example, a freelance graphic designer who balances her projects with managing bipolar II disorder. Her mornings begin with meditation and a light workout, which she says "kicks off my day on a positive note." Work follows, but she breaks every hour for five minutes to stretch or do breathing exercises, keeping stress levels in check. Evenings are for relaxation—reading, cooking, or photography.

Then there's Michael, a high school teacher, who finds stability in the very structure of his job. His weekdays are rigorously scheduled with teaching, planning, and grading, but he reserves his evenings for quiet time with his family, which he calls his "daily dose of happiness." Weekends are less structured to allow for spontaneity, giving him a balance between routine and relaxation.

These examples underscore that while the specifics of a routine will vary, the essence remains the same: a blend of structure and flexibility that supports both the management of bipolar disorder and the pursuit of personal fulfillment. Remember, the goal of a routine isn't to confine you but to liberate you, providing a framework within which you can live more freely and fully, even amidst the ups and downs of bipolar disorder. So, take these ideas, tailor them to your life, and start building your own rhythm that makes your daily symphony more harmonious.

5.2 Mindfulness and Meditation: Tools for Emotional Regulation

Let's talk about mindfulness and meditation—two buzzwords you've probably heard tossed around like confetti at a New Year's party. But beyond the hype, these practices are like secret weapons for anyone grappling with the emotional roller coaster of bipolar disorder. Mindfulness isn't just a trendy practice; it's about anchoring yourself in the present moment, which can be a game-changer when your emotions seem determined to throw you off balance.

Imagine you're a surfer. Each wave represents a different emotion or thought. Mindfulness teaches you to ride these waves without getting pulled under by the current of your thoughts or moods. It's about observing these waves—acknowledging their presence without letting them dictate where you go. This kind of emotional regulation is crucial in bipolar disorder, where your mood can shift dramatically and sometimes unpredictably. Practicing mindfulness can increase awareness of these shifts, often gaining precious moments to make informed decisions rather than being swept away.

Incorporating mindfulness into your daily life doesn't require sitting cross-legged for hours or chanting mantras—unless that's your jam. It can be as simple as taking a mindful walk. Try to notice each step the next time you walk to your mailbox or around the neighborhood. Feel your foot as it meets the ground, the rhythm of your breath, the sounds around you. This isn't just about enjoying a walk; it's about training your mind to stay focused on the present, which can significantly reduce stress and anxiety.

Now, let's dial into meditation. If mindfulness is about staying present during your daily activities, meditation is the workout session for your mind. It strengthens your ability to concentrate and calm your mind. Starting a meditation practice can be as simple as dedicating five minutes daily to sit quietly and focus on your breath. When thoughts intrude—and they will—gently acknowledge them and then bring your focus back to your breathing. Over time, these few minutes can expand, and the calmness and focus you cultivate during these sessions can spill over into the rest of your day.

Ample resources exist for those wondering how to deepen their practice or learn more about integrating these tools into their life. Apps like Headspace or Calm offer guided meditations and are perfect for beginners. They take you through the basics and gradually help you build a meditation practice that can withstand the busyness of modern life. Books like "Wherever You Go, There You Are" by Jon Kabat-Zinn can provide deeper insights into mindfulness, enriching your understanding and practice. For those who prefer a more structured learning environment, local community centers or wellness clinics often offer courses in mindfulness and meditation, providing guided instruction and community support.

Tapping into mindfulness and meditation opens up a new way to handle the complexities of bipolar disorder, offering tools that enhance stability, promote mental clarity, and foster a greater sense of peace. You're surviving and thriving by incorporating these practices into your life—riding the waves with skill, grace, and resilience. So why not give it a try? Start small, stay consistent, and watch how these ancient practices can bring modern benefits to your life, transforming challenges into opportunities for growth and self-discovery.

Building a Support Network: Finding and Nurturing Relationships

Think of your support network as your personal cheerleading squad, emergency response team, and wisdom council all rolled into one. When you're dealing with bipolar disorder, these are the folks who will pass you tissues, share a laugh, or give that sage piece of advice when you need it most. The importance of this network can't be overstressed—it's a core part of not just surviving with bipolar disorder but genuinely thriving.

First off, let's chat about why a robust support network is such a big deal. Imagine you're trying to lift a heavy box. Doing it alone could be challenging, maybe even risky. But with a team, not only is the load lighter, but it's also less likely to drop on your toes. Similarly, a support network lightens the emotional and practical burdens of bipolar disorder. During a manic phase, they can help keep your feet on the ground. In a depressive episode, they're there to lift you up. And on the days when you're feeling just fine, they're there to share in the joy. It's about having a safety net and a sounding board, ensuring you're supported, no matter what the bipolar skies look like.

Now, identifying who makes it into your support squad is crucial. Not everyone will understand what you're going through, and that's okay. Start with those who've shown empathy and patience and were calm in previous storms. These might be friends, family members, or even coworkers. The key is their ability to provide support without judgment. A good litmus test is to think about how you feel after spending time with them. They might not fit your support network best if you leave feeling drained or anxious. But you're on the right track if you feel uplifted, understood, or simply calm.

But it's not just about who is already in your life. Sometimes, expanding your network can bring new perspectives and understanding. This is where support groups and online communities come into play. These groups are like finding a whole tribe of people who get it because they're walking similar paths. They can be invaluable sources of advice, empathy, and understanding. Whether it's a local meetup or an online forum, these communities can make you feel less alone in your struggles. They provide a platform to share experiences and tips and sometimes to vent in a space where others instinctively understand the highs and lows.

Maintaining these relationships is where the real work comes in. It's not just about having people around; it's about nurturing those connections. Communication is your best tool here. Be open about what you're experiencing and what kind of support you need. It might be someone to accompany you to a doctor's appointment, help with daily tasks when you're low, or simply a friend to call when you need to talk. Setting clear boundaries is also part of this communication. Let your support network know what is helpful and what is not, and be open to hearing their needs, too. Remember, these relationships are a two-way street. Just as you need support, you also need to be supportive.

Consider also the power of gratitude in these relationships. A simple thank you, a note, or a small gesture to show appreciation can go a long way in keeping the bonds strong. It's about showing that you value their support and reciprocating in ways that strengthen the relationship.

Building and maintaining a support network is like tending a garden. It takes patience, effort, and care, but the blooms that result can brighten even the darkest days. These relationships provide a buffer against the storms of bipolar disorder, offering light, warmth, and shelter. By investing in this network, you're not just creating a safety net but also enriching your life, making each day a little easier, brighter, and more connected.

5.4 Workplace Strategies: Thriving Professionally

When it comes to managing bipolar disorder in the professional arena, think of it as orchestrating a well-timed dance between your personal needs and your professional responsibilities. The workplace can either be a stage for triumphs or a battleground for challenges, and much of that depends on how you navigate the complexities of disclosure, accommodations, stress management, and career development. Let's unpack these elements, ensuring you're equipped to survive in your career and thrive.

Disclosure and Privacy

Deciding whether to disclose your bipolar disorder at work is akin to choosing whether to share a personal secret with a colleague—it can strengthen your connection and lead to support, or it can change dynamics in unpredictable ways. It's a highly personal decision, often influenced by your workplace environment, the nature of your job, and the severity of your symptoms. If your bipolar disorder significantly affects your job performance, disclosing it might be necessary to seek accommodations. However, this comes with considerations for privacy and the potential for stigma.

Navigating this decision requires understanding your legal protections. In many places, laws like the Americans with Disabilities Act (ADA) in the U.S. protect employees from discrimination based on disability and require employers to provide reasonable accommodations. However, these protections only kick in once a condition is disclosed officially. It's wise to weigh the benefits of potential support against the risks of possible stigma or misunderstanding. If you choose to disclose, consider doing so in a structured way—perhaps during a meeting with your HR representative, where you can discuss your condition and how it might be effectively managed at work. This approach protects your privacy while setting a professional tone for the conversation.

Accommodations for Bipolar Disorder

Once disclosure is out of the way, the next step is to consider what accommodations might help you manage your bipolar disorder while maintaining your productivity. Accommodations can vary widely depending on your specific needs and the nature of your job. They might include flexible scheduling to attend doctor's appointments, the ability to work from home on days when symptoms are particularly challenging, or adjustments to your workspace to reduce stress and distractions.

For example, if you find that a noisy office environment triggers anxiety or makes it difficult to concentrate during depressive episodes, requesting a quieter workspace or noise-canceling headphones could be reasonable accommodations. Similarly, if sleep disruptions associated with your condition leave you drained, a flexible start time could help you manage your health without compromising your work responsibilities. The key is identifying which aspects of your job interact with your symptoms and seeking accommodations that directly address these intersections, facilitating a balance that supports your health and professional performance.

Managing Stress at Work

Stress management in the workplace is crucial since high stress can exacerbate bipolar symptoms, potentially leading to a cycle of mood instability and decreased productivity. Developing effective stress management techniques can be your shield against such cycles. Simple strategies like organized task management—using tools like digital calendars or to-do list apps—can help keep you on track without feeling overwhelmed. Regular breaks are also essential; a few minutes away from your desk to breathe deeply or stretch can significantly reduce stress levels.

Moreover, establishing clear boundaries around work hours and responsibilities can prevent the kind of overcommitment that leads to burnout. It's important to communicate openly with your supervisor about your workload and to advocate for a balance that supports your well-being. Remember, being proactive about stress management helps maintain stability and enhances your overall effectiveness and job satisfaction.

Career Development

Finally, managing bipolar disorder doesn't mean putting your professional aspirations on hold. It's entirely possible to advance your career and achieve your goals. This might involve seeking roles with a better work-life balance, pursuing further education to expand your qualifications, or finding a mentor who understands your unique challenges and can provide guidance and support.

Career development can also mean learning to leverage your strengths. Many individuals with bipolar disorder find that they are exceptionally creative, empathetic, or driven—traits that can be significant assets in many professional contexts. By focusing on roles that capitalize on these strengths, you can manage your condition more effectively and excel in your chosen field.

In navigating these professional waters, remember that managing bipolar disorder at work is not just about overcoming challenges; it's about leveraging your full potential, advocating for your needs, and building a fulfilling career that acknowledges and supports your mental health. With the right strategies, you can thrive professionally, not despite your bipolar disorder but in conjunction with managing it effectively.

5.5 Financial Management: Planning and Stability

Navigating the financial waters when you've got bipolar disorder riding shotgun can sometimes feel like trying to budget for a road trip without knowing the distance or the cost of gas. Especially when you factor in the price of treatments and the possibility of income fluctuations during episodes, having a sound financial plan isn't just helpful—it's crucial. It's about more than keeping your bank account in the green; it's about reducing financial stress that could worsen symptoms.

So, how do you start? Think of financial planning as building a dam to keep your resources flowing steadily, even when the weather changes unexpectedly. The first step is understanding the full scope of potential costs associated with bipolar disorder. These could range from medications and therapy sessions to possible hospital stays. It's a lot, but don't let it overwhelm you. Instead, break it down into manageable chunks. Start by listing these expenses and then assess your health insurance coverage. What's covered, what's not, and where might you need additional help? This clarity can be incredibly empowering and can prevent nasty surprises down the road.

Next up, let's talk budgeting—your financial roadmap. A budget accommodating your medical needs and regular expenses can help you avoid financial strain. Start by tracking your income and expenses for a month or two. See where your money is going, and identify areas where you can cut back without sacrificing your well-being. There are plenty of budgeting tools and apps out there that can make this process easier. Apps like Mint or YNAB (You Need A Budget) link to your financial accounts and automatically categorize your spending, making it easier to stick to your budget and spot trends over time.

Let's address the elephant in the room—impulsive spending during manic episodes. This cannot be easy when you are browsing at 3 am. It's like being on a shopping spree with a blindfold. To curb this, set up safeguards. One strategy might be to have a trusted friend or family member keep an eye on your spending. Some even go as far as arranging with their bank to require dual authorization for purchases above a certain amount during these phases. It's about creating a safety net that respects your independence while protecting you from potential financial harm.

Financial assistance resources are another critical piece of the puzzle. Many are unaware of the programs available to help manage the costs of medication and therapy. Pharmaceutical companies often offer patient assistance programs for medications, providing them at a lower price or even free to those who qualify. Websites like NeedyMeds provide information on such programs. Moreover, for therapy costs, organizations like the National Alliance on Mental

Illness (NAMI) and local mental health clinics often offer resources or sliding-scale payment options based on income. Don't hesitate to reach out to these resources; they can provide a financial breather, allowing you to focus more on managing your health and less on managing your wallet.

Incorporating these financial management strategies into your life can create a buffer against the economic uncertainties of living with bipolar disorder. By taking control of your finances through careful planning, budgeting, and utilizing available resources, you not only safeguard your financial well-being but also reduce a significant source of stress, making your path a little smoother. And in a world that often feels like it's spinning a bit too fast, having that extra stability can make all the difference. So, take the wheel, set your course, and let's navigate these financial waters together, ensuring that you stay afloat even when the tides try to pull you under.

5.6 Creativity and Hobbies: Channeling Energy Positively

Let's paint a colorful picture here—imagine your creativity as a vibrant palette of paints, each shade representing a different aspect of your personality and potential. For those living with bipolar disorder, engaging in creative activities isn't just a way to pass the time; it's a form of therapy, a means of self-expression, and a powerful tool for managing the emotional spectrum that comes with the condition. Whether it's art, writing, music, or digging your hands into the earth of your garden, these activities offer more than just distraction—they provide a channel for turbulent and serene emotions. As I mentioned earlier, I'm not an artist, but art in the context of therapy is not about the quality of the art but about expressing yourself and letting the process of creating be like unpacking a suitcase full of things you didn't even know were there.

Think of times when manic energy feels like an electrical storm inside you. It's intense, buzzing, seemingly uncontainable. Now, imagine channeling that energy into painting a canvas, composing a piece of music, or writing a story. These creative outlets allow you to 'plug-in' that surging energy and transform it into something beautiful or at least meaningful. It's not about suppressing what you feel but redirecting it into something that doesn't just consume you but contributes to your world. The therapeutic benefits of these activities are well-documented. They can elevate your mood, decrease anxiety, and provide a sense of accomplishment and self-worth that are invaluable on days when the disorder tries to convince you otherwise.

Incorporating these hobbies and creative pursuits into your daily routine isn't about filling every spare minute with activity to ward off potential mood swings. It's about balance and fulfillment. Establishing a routine that includes time set aside for creativity can act as a stabilizing force. It creates a predictable, safe space each day for self-expression. This scheduled creativity time becomes a ritual, a checkpoint, a familiar friend that waits for you regardless of the day you're having. It's comforting to know that no matter the storm, there's a harbor where you can anchor, focus, and channel your thoughts and emotions in a productive, stabilizing way.

Take Vincent van Gogh, Sylvia Plath, Virginia Woolf, Frida Kahlo, etc. These well-known artists created some of their most iconic works while battling various mental illnesses. These are just a few examples, but countless other artists have channeled their struggles with mental illness into their creative work, producing deeply personal, emotionally resonant, and persistently influential art.

Now, let's draw inspiration from those who have turned their bipolar disorder into a driving force for their creativity, achieving significant accomplishments along the way. Take the example of a renowned author who channels her manic energy into writing novels, her rapid thoughts and boundless energy fueling her vibrant narratives. Or consider a musician whose deepest, most resonant songs were composed in the depths of a depressive phase, capturing emotions that strike a chord with others. These stories aren't just individual successes; they're beacons of possibility, showing that the energy and perspective of bipolar disorder can be powerful catalysts for creative achievement.

These narratives are important. They shift the story from one of struggle to one of potential. They show that while bipolar disorder is undoubtedly a challenging companion, it can also be a dynamic, creative ally if channeled appropriately. So, whether you're sketching in a notepad, strumming a guitar, or crafting poetry, remember these are more than hobbies; they are tools in your wellness kit, ways to balance your life, and channels to turn your experiences into art, insight, or simply, a release.

As this chapter closes, remember that integrating creativity and hobbies into your life is not just about managing bipolar disorder; it's about enriching your entire existence. These activities provide a unique way to balance your emotional world, offering both stability and a source of deep, personal fulfillment. They allow you to gracefully navigate the highs and lows, using the very energy of your symptoms to fuel your creative fire. Keep this canvas of opportunity ready, and paint your journey with the broad strokes of persistence, the detailed touches of self-awareness, and the vibrant colors of creativity. As we turn the page, let's carry forward this creative spirit, exploring further how personal growth and transformation are not just possible but within reach, even as we continue to manage and thrive with bipolar disorder.

CHAPTER:6
NAVIGATING RELATIONSHIPS AND BIPOLAR

Try explaining to someone why you rearranged your entire living room at 3 AM, wearing the same superhero costume for a week straight...or disappearing for three days. It sounds like a quirky sitcom plot, right? But when you have bipolar disorder, these scenarios can be real life and not always as humorous to explain to loved ones. Navigating relationships when you have bipolar disorder is a bit like being a translator, constantly trying to translate your feelings and actions into a language that your loved ones can understand. This chapter dives into the ocean of relationship dynamics, fishing out the best communication strategies and showing you how to maintain a healthy social fleet, even when the bipolar seas get choppy.

6.1 Communication is Key: Talking About Bipolar with Loved Ones

The Role of Open Dialogue

Open dialogue about your bipolar disorder isn't just about keeping people informed; it's about letting them in. It's about turning what could be a monologue of internal struggles into a dialogue of shared understanding and support. Think of it like opening the doors to a secret garden – you're allowing someone to step into a part of your world that's intensely personal. This isn't just beneficial; it's transformative. It transforms isolation into intimacy and misconceptions into mutual understanding. By talking openly about your bipolar disorder, you're not just seeking sympathy but forging empathy, which is a far stronger foundation for any relationship.

But why is this so crucial? Because bipolar disorder doesn't just affect you. It ripples out, touching everyone in your life in some way. When those closest to you understand what you're going through, they're better equipped to offer the proper support when needed. They can recognize the signs that you're entering a manic or depressive phase before you do and can gently help steer you back, akin to a co-pilot helping to navigate through turbulent weather.

Effective Communication Techniques

Now, let's talk tactics. Effective communication about your bipolar disorder doesn't mean just blurting out everything during a family dinner—timing, tone, and transparency matter. Start by choosing a good time when you and your loved one are relaxed and there's enough time to dig deep. Use "I" statements, such as "I feel..." or "I experience..." to keep the conversation subjective and non-accusatory. This helps keep defenses down and empathy up.

It's also helpful to be as specific as possible about what bipolar disorder means for you. Everyone's experience with bipolar disorder is unique. Describe your symptoms, your triggers, and what adequate support looks like for you. Maybe bring a cheat sheet — a list of bullet points to ensure you cover the essentials without getting overwhelmed or sidetracked.

Setting Boundaries

While we're unpacking the communication toolkit, let's talk about boundaries. Setting healthy boundaries is like drawing a clear map of where you end and others begin. It's crucial because it protects your energy and emotions, preventing relationships from becoming draining or one-sided. Clear boundaries might look like saying no to social events when you're feeling low or asking for space during high-anxiety periods. It's not about building walls; it's about installing gates where needed, gates you can open when you choose.

And remember, setting boundaries is a two-way street. Just as you need your boundaries respected, you should respect the boundaries of others. This mutual respect creates a balanced relationship where both parties feel safe and valued.

Navigating Misunderstandings

Finally, let's tackle the big one: misunderstandings. They're inevitable, like rain at a picnic. Misunderstandings can stem from a lack of information, differences in perspective, or the unpredictable nature of bipolar disorder itself. When these occur, it's like hitting a pothole on the road; it can jolt you, but it doesn't have to derail the journey.

When a misunderstanding arises, address it directly and calmly. Re-explain your perspective if needed, and be open to hearing theirs. Sometimes, just acknowledging that bipolar disorder can make things confusing for everyone helps. Having a previously agreed-upon plan for handling conflicts is also beneficial, like taking a time-out to cool down or using a safe word when things get too heated.

Navigating relationships with bipolar disorder is no small feat, but with open communication, effective techniques, clear boundaries, and strategies for handling misunderstandings, you can maintain and even strengthen your connections. It's about turning challenges into opportunities for growth, understanding, and deeper bonding. And isn't that what relationships are all about? Growing together, understanding each other, and strengthening bonds? So, let's keep the dialogue open, the boundaries clear, and the understanding deep. With these tools, you're well-equipped to maintain healthy, supportive relationships, no matter how choppy the bipolar seas might get.

6.2 When Bipolar Strains Relationships: Coping Strategies for Couples

Navigating a romantic relationship can often feel like dancing a delicate tango, where every step and turn must be in sync. Throw bipolar disorder into the mix, and that dance can sometimes feel more like a mosh pit at a rock concert, where unpredictability is the only expectation. The truth is that bipolar disorder introduces a set of challenges that can test the strongest of partnerships. It can stretch the fabric of intimacy, twist the dynamics of interaction, and add an intense strain on both partners. Recognizing these challenges is the first step towards managing them, not just for the sake of maintaining the relationship but for nurturing it to grow stronger and more resilient in the face of adversity.

The impact of bipolar disorder on a relationship can manifest in several ways. Mood swings can create sudden extremes of emotional climates, sometimes warm and sunny, other times cold and stormy. This unpredictability can be confusing and exhausting for a partner who might feel they're constantly walking on eggshells. During manic episodes, increased impulsivity or grandiosity can lead to decisions that strain the relationship, from extravagant spending sprees to emotional outbursts. Conversely, during depressive phases, the withdrawal and lack of energy can leave partners feeling sidelined, helpless, or neglected. The key here is understanding these impacts and actively working together to mitigate them.

One effective strategy for couples navigating these turbulent waters is couples therapy. It's like having a skilled guide for your relationship journey, someone who can help map out the emotional terrain of bipolar disorder and equip both partners with the tools they need to navigate it. Therapy provides a neutral ground to explore sensitive issues, improve communication skills, and strengthen emotional connections. It's about expressing needs and frustrations without blame and listening empathetically. Couple therapy can also be a space to develop strategies tailored to your relationship, helping you foresee and manage potential conflicts arising from bipolar symptoms.

Establishing routines can also play a crucial role in stabilizing relationship dynamics. Just as personal routines aid in managing bipolar disorder, relationship routines can help maintain a sense of normalcy and security. This could be as simple as setting aside time daily to connect without distractions, engaging in a shared hobby, or maintaining a date night each week. These routines become shared anchors, points of stability, and predictability amidst the unpredictability of bipolar disorder. They offer moments of connection that can reinforce the partnership, providing reassurance and continuity that can be crucial during challenging times.

Maintaining intimacy is another crucial aspect, often directly impacted by the symptoms of bipolar disorder. The fluctuations in emotional and physical intimacy can be one of the most challenging aspects for couples. During manic or depressive episodes, sexual desire can either spike or plummet, creating mismatches in libido that can frustrate both partners. Open discussions about sexual needs and expectations can help, as can scheduling intimacy in some cases, which might not sound romantic but can be surprisingly effective in ensuring both partners' needs are met. It's also essential to foster emotional intimacy, ensuring that physical closeness is just one aspect of a deeper emotional connection. Small gestures of affection, active listening, and verbal affirmations of love and commitment can all nurture this emotional closeness, maintaining a bond that physical intimacy alone cannot sustain.

Lastly, the role of external support systems cannot be overstated. No couple is an island; sometimes, the best support comes from outside the relationship. Encouraging each other to maintain individual friendships and hobbies can provide external outlets and perspectives that enhance personal well-being and, by extension, relationship health. Support groups for couples dealing with bipolar disorder can also be invaluable, offering a community that understands and shares similar challenges. These groups can provide practical advice and emotional support, reduce feelings of isolation, and provide examples of successful coping strategies.

In essence, managing bipolar disorder within a relationship is about teamwork, where both partners actively engage in strategies that foster understanding, stability, and growth. It's about turning challenges into opportunities to strengthen the bond, ensuring the relationship survives and thrives. By embracing therapies, establishing routines, maintaining open communication about intimacy, and leveraging external supports, couples can navigate the complexities of bipolar disorder together, preserving the harmony and deepening the connection that initially brought them together.

6.3 Parenting with Bipolar: Guidance and Support Strategies

Parenting is akin to being a superhero; it's a role filled with challenges, rewards, and the occasional need to save the day. When you add bipolar disorder into the mix, the cape feels a bit heavier, and the days can sometimes seem a bit more daunting. But fear not because, with the right strategies, you can navigate the complexities of parenting with bipolar disorder, ensuring that you manage your health while providing a loving, stable environment for your kids.

Let's talk about balancing parenting and bipolar management. Imagine you're juggling—each ball represents different aspects of your life: one for parenting, one for work, another for personal relationships, and a brightly colored one for managing bipolar disorder. Keeping all these in the air can be tricky, especially when the bipolar ball feels like it's made of lead some days. The key here is not to prioritize one ball over the others but to learn techniques that help you juggle them more effectively. This starts with a solid routine that includes time for medication, therapy sessions, and rest. It's also crucial to stay vigilant about your symptoms; being proactive about managing your health can prevent your symptoms from overshadowing your parenting. Maintain open lines of communication with your mental health provider about how parenting impacts your bipolar disorder and vice versa. This ongoing dialogue can help tailor your treatment plan to fit your lifestyle as a parent better.

Communicating with children about bipolar disorder can feel as tricky as explaining why the sky is blue; it's complex but not impossible. The goal is to provide them with honesty, reassurance, and support. Start by considering your child's age and maturity level. Younger kids need more straightforward explanations—perhaps explaining that sometimes you have "big feelings" or "energy days" and other times you might feel "slow" or "sad." It's like explaining weather patterns: sunny days, stormy days, and everything. For older children and teenagers, you can share more detailed information, perhaps comparing bipolar disorder to a medical condition that requires ongoing treatment, much like diabetes or hypertension. Regardless of age, reassure them that your mood changes are not their fault, nor are they responsible for managing them. This reassurance can be a massive relief for kids who may not fully understand the complexities of mental health.

Creating a supportive family environment is crucial. This doesn't mean turning your home into a fortress but setting up structures that foster stability. Routines are potent for children; they provide security and normalcy. Keep regular meal times, bedtimes, and family activities, even if your mood fluctuates. These predictable patterns can be comforting, not just for your children but for you as well. Also, consider having a plan in place for times when your bipolar disorder might disrupt this routine. This could involve arranging for a family member or a trusted friend to step in when you need to focus on your health. Additionally, have emergency plans that your children understand, such as who to call if they need help when you cannot provide it due to your symptoms.

Seeking and accepting help might be among the toughest yet most critical strategies. It's not uncommon to feel like you have to do it all, especially as a parent. But remember, asking for help isn't a sign of weakness—it's an act of strength. When things feel overwhelming, lean on your partner, relatives, or close friends to share the load. Professional services like therapists or parenting counselors can provide guidance and support tailored to your needs. Moreover, consider joining support groups for parents with bipolar disorder. Sharing your experiences and hearing others' can give practical advice and emotional solace that you're not alone in this journey.

In navigating the dual challenges of parenting and managing bipolar disorder, remember that perfection is not the goal; presence is. It's about being there, doing your best, and showing up for your kids, even on days when you don't feel like you can. By managing your health, communicating openly, creating a supportive environment, and seeking help when needed, you're not just surviving as a parent with bipolar disorder; you're thriving, providing your children with the resilience and understanding they need to navigate their own lives.

6.4 Supporting a Partner or Family Member with Bipolar

Stepping into the shoes of someone who supports a loved one with bipolar disorder is a bit like becoming an impromptu juggler at a circus. One moment, you're a spectator, and the next, you're keeping several balls in the air—emotional support, daily responsibilities, and sometimes crisis management—all while trying to maintain your own balance. Understanding bipolar disorder from the outside involves recognizing that this isn't just a series of mood swings but a complex and enduring condition that your loved one battles with. It requires a deep dive into the symptoms, which fluctuate from the highs of mania to the lows of depression, each bringing its own set of challenges.

For starters, education is vital. The more you know about bipolar disorder, the better equipped you are to provide support that's both effective and empathetic. Recognize the symptoms that come with each phase. Manic episodes might include increased energy, less need for sleep, and sometimes reckless behavior, while depressive episodes can bring overwhelming sadness, fatigue, and withdrawal. Understanding these signs helps you to not misinterpret these behaviors as personal or intentional but as part of a medical condition.

Now, let's talk about the fine line between supporting and enabling. It's like knowing when to offer a helping hand and when to encourage them to walk on their own. For instance, during a manic phase, it might be instinctive to want to protect your loved one from impulsive decisions. However, it's crucial to encourage strategies they can employ, like discussing a spending limit or identifying activities that channel their energy in healthier ways. In contrast, during depressive episodes, support might look like ensuring they're not isolating themselves excessively while respecting their need for space and quiet. It's about empowerment, not control—helping them manage their symptoms without taking over their responsibilities, which can undermine their confidence and ability to cope independently.

Caring for the caregiver—you—is not just a sidebar in this narrative; it's central to the plot. Supporting someone with bipolar disorder can be draining, both emotionally and physically. You must carve out time for self-care, ensuring you don't burn out. Set boundaries that help you maintain a healthy balance. This might mean setting times when you focus on your own needs or hobbies, or it might involve seeking support from others, such as friends, family, or support groups. As an emergency oxygen mask on a plane, you must secure your mask before assisting others. This ensures you have the strength and emotional capacity to support your loved one's needs.

Preparing for emergencies is another critical aspect. Bipolar disorder can sometimes lead to crises, such as severe depressive episodes or even suicidal ideation. Having a plan in place can be a lifesaver. This includes knowing when and how to contact healthcare providers, understanding what to say and do in a crisis, and having a list of emergency contacts, including close friends, family, or a therapist. It's like having a map and a first aid kit ready; you hope never to need them, but should the situation arise, you're prepared. This preparation provides a practical framework for handling such situations and gives you peace of mind, knowing you're not navigating this terrain without tools.

Supporting a loved one with bipolar disorder is a profound journey of love, patience, and understanding. It requires you to be informed, empathetic, and resilient. You ensure your support is sustainable and effective by educating yourself, balancing supporting and enabling, caring for your emotional needs, and preparing for potential crises. Remember, your role is pivotal— helping your loved one manage their disorder and walking alongside them with strength, compassion, and hope, making the journey less daunting for you both.

6.5 The Social Life Spectrum: Maintaining Friendships

Managing friendships when you're juggling the highs and lows of bipolar disorder can sometimes feel like trying to sing a duet solo—tricky, if not downright disheartening. The challenges are real, from the urge to hibernate during a depressive spell to the whirlwind of over-sharing during a manic phase. It's like your social skills are on a seesaw, and finding that balance is imperative to maintaining meaningful relationships that don't just survive but thrive, even in the face of bipolar disorder.

Let's unpack this, starting with the challenges. When you're low, the world seems to be moving slowly, and isolation is the only comforting response. It's not that you don't value your friends; it's just that the energy required to engage can feel as draining as running a marathon. On the flip side, during manic episodes, you might find yourself the life of the party, but the intensity can be overwhelming for others, and impulsivity can lead to actions that strain friendships. These fluctuations can make friendships feel like a roller-coaster ride for which not everyone is strapped in.

Building and nurturing friendships requires a toolkit, not just good intentions. Transparency is your first tool. It involves being honest about your bipolar disorder with close friends. This doesn't mean your condition needs to be the center of every conversation. However, letting friends know what you're dealing with can demystify your behaviors and help them understand your needs and boundaries. For instance, explaining that sometimes you need to step back for self-care during depressive episodes can help them understand your absences aren't about them. It's about caring for your mental health.

Communication, your next tool, is about keeping the lines open. Regular check-ins with friends, even if it's just a text or a shared meme, can keep the connection alive even when you're not up for social outings. It's also about expressing appreciation for their patience and understanding, which can reinforce their support and willingness to stand by you. Mutual support is crucial; it's a two-way street. Just as you appreciate their understanding, offering an empathetic ear or support during their times of need can strengthen the bond, making the friendship a shared refuge and joy, not just a support group.

Now, let's talk about social activities. Choosing suitable activities can play a significant role in managing your symptoms while still engaging with friends. Opt for low-pressure environments that allow you to engage at your own pace. Group activities like art classes, book clubs, or nature walks can be great because they offer both social interaction and the opportunity to withdraw into the activity when you feel overwhelmed. These settings can be less emotionally demanding but provide the social stimulation crucial for mental health.

Dealing with rejection or loss of friendships is perhaps the most challenging part. Not everyone will understand or stick around, and that's a tough pill to swallow. It's important to grieve these losses, to allow yourself to feel the sadness or frustration, and to recognize that it's not a reflection of your worth. Friendships can end for many reasons, and bipolar disorder might be one factor. The key is to cherish the friends who stick around, those who accept you with all your facets, and remain open to new relationships. Remember, the quality of friendships often matters much more than quantity. Each true friend is a treasure, a vital piece of your support network that helps you navigate the complexities of life with bipolar disorder.

Operating in the social spectrum with bipolar disorder isn't about perfection; it's about effort, understanding, and a bit of strategy. By being honest, maintaining communication, choosing the correct social settings, and handling losses gracefully, you can cultivate a circle of friends that enriches your life and anchors you through the storms. Friendships, like gardens, require tending, and with the proper care, even a garden touched by the wild swings of bipolar disorder can flourish, bringing color and joy to your life.

6.6 Bipolar and Isolation: Breaking the Cycle

Let's face it, sometimes dealing with bipolar disorder feels a bit like you're a smartphone in airplane mode: disconnected from the world and not entirely functioning at total capacity. Isolation isn't just about being alone; it's a whole mood, and for someone with bipolar disorder, it can be a frequent guest. The reasons? They're as complex as a well-aged bourbon. Stigma, for starters, plays a significant role. That pesky voice whispers, "They won't understand," or "They'll think you're crazy," pushing you to pull back from social interactions. Then there's the internal duo of fear and judgment, always ready to party, making you doubt every social impulse you have. And let's not forget the symptoms themselves— when you're riding the highs of mania or sinking into the lows of depression, reaching out can feel as daunting as skydiving without a parachute.

But here's the kicker: isolation, while it might feel comforting at the moment, can feed into the very symptoms you're trying to manage. It's a classic catch-22. The good news? You can break this cycle. It starts with understanding the triggers for your withdrawal. Is it anxiety about being judged? Exhaustion from doing emotional gymnastics? Identifying these triggers is like being handed a map in a dense forest; it doesn't clear the trees but shows you a path out.

Now, let's move on to strategies to dodge the isolation bullet. First up, support groups. These aren't just about sitting in a circle and sharing your deepest fears (though that can be part of it). They're about finding your tribe, people who nod and say, "Me too" instead of "Really?" These groups provide a platform to connect, share experiences, and offer mutual support, whether face-to-face or online. It's like having a safety net for people who get it.

Community activities can also be a game-changer. Think about what you love doing or something you've always wanted to try. Photography? Hiking? Cooking? Community classes or groups focused on these interests can be a double win. You get to do something you enjoy (or think you might want) and meet people with similar interests. It's socializing with a side of distraction, which can make it feel less intense and more manageable.

Online socialization is another tool in your kit. In the digital age, connecting with others can be as easy as tapping on a screen. Online forums, social media groups, or even gaming communities can offer connections that don't require you to leave your comfort zone physically. It's like dipping your toes in the social pool without diving headfirst. Just be mindful of the nature of these interactions and aim for healthy, supportive connections.

Lastly, let's talk about reaching out. Sometimes, the most challenging part of dealing with isolation is taking that first step to connect or reconnect with others. Whether it's a text to a friend you haven't spoken to in a while, joining a new online forum, or even seeking out a mental health professional, each action can be a step away from isolation. Remember, reaching out is not a sign of weakness; it's an act of strength. It's acknowledging that everyone needs a helping hand sometimes. And in most cases, people are more understanding and supportive than you might fear.

Crafting a personalized plan to combat isolation can serve as your roadmap. Start by listing your triggers and the signs that you're withdrawing. Then, detail steps you can take when you notice these signs, like reaching out to a friend, attending a support group, or engaging in a community activity. Also, list the people and resources you can turn to for support. Having this plan written down can make it feel more concrete and more doable. It's like having a recipe; you might not follow it to the letter every time, but it gives you a foundation to start from, and sometimes, that's all you need to get the ball rolling.

In wrapping up this discussion on isolation and bipolar disorder, remember this: isolation can be a part of living with bipolar disorder, but it doesn't have to define your experience. I know I wrote about communication in an earlier chapter, but I cannot stress enough the importance of open communication. By understanding its roots, employing strategies to maintain connections, reaching out when needed, and having a plan, you can keep the doors open to the world around you, ensuring that isolation is a visitor, not a permanent resident. As we close this chapter and look ahead, let's carry forward the theme of connection—not just as a strategy but as a way of life, enriching our journey and enhancing our resilience in managing bipolar disorder. Let's stay connected, stay engaged, and continue supporting each other in every way possible.

CHAPTER:7
ADDRESSING STIGMA AND BUILDING ADVOCACY

Imagine you're at a party, and instead of saying, "Hi, I'm Jane, I like hiking, and I'm allergic to peanuts," you say, "Hi, I'm Jane, and I have bipolar disorder." You can almost hear the record scratch, right? That's stigma for you—turning what could be a conversation into a conversation stopper. Stigma is like that unwelcome party guest who whispers tall tales about you in every corner of the room. It's pervasive, sticky, and, frankly, a real pain to deal with. But here's where we start changing the tune, turning down the volume on stigma and cranking up the dialogue on advocacy. In this chapter, we will unpack the suitcase of stigma, lay everything out, and see how we can fold it up neatly into something manageable, maybe even something positive.

7.1 Fighting the Stigma: Strategies for Personal Advocacy

Understanding Stigma

Stigma doesn't materialize out of thin air. It's woven from threads of misunderstanding, fear, and stereotypes, all dyed in the deep hues of historical prejudice. It's like a bad game of telephone; somewhere along the line, the message about what bipolar disorder is got garbled up with myths, leading to a lot of confused and harmful perceptions. These perceptions can manifest in various arenas of life, causing individuals to hesitate before seeking help or, worse, to face discrimination in their social circles, workplaces, and even healthcare settings. For example, "Mental illness is due to drug or alcohol abuse."; or "Folks on disability due to mental health are living comfortably at taxpayers' expense"; "Depressed people are just weak."; "Depressed people need to try harder, pray more, snap out of it"; "Mental illness means constant hospitalization, homelessness, unemployment."

The media hasn't always been the best ally, either. How often have you seen a movie where the 'crazy' character is the villain or the comic relief, and they happen to have bipolar disorder? Quite a few, right? These portrayals stick in people's minds, coloring their perceptions of what bipolar disorder is, which leads to stigma. It'speopl a cycle that perpetuates itself, keeping those with the disorder in the shadows, often ashamed and isolated.

Personal Advocacy Techniques

So, how do you fight this Goliath? Start with the stone of knowledge. Educating yourself about bipolar disorder is like arming yourself with a shield; it protects you from internalizing the stigma and prepares you to educate others. The more you know, the more you can challenge the myths when you encounter them. Speaking of challenges, personal advocacy is all about speaking up. It's about correcting misconceptions when you hear them and sharing your own experiences if you're comfortable. Imagine turning your story into a bridge for understanding. By sharing, you humanize the condition and turn statistics into a face, a voice, and a story—stories are harder to ignore or stigmatize.

Role of Language in Combating Stigma

Never underestimate the power of words. They can build worlds or tear them down. When talking about bipolar disorder, the words you choose matter. Instead of saying someone is 'bipolar,' it's more respectful to say someone 'has bipolar disorder.' Why? Because their condition defines no one. It's about putting the person before the disorder, emphasizing that having bipolar disorder is just one aspect of their being. This might seem like a slight shift, but it's powerful because it challenges the subconscious notions that link identity closely with disorder.

Engagement in Advocacy Activities

If you're feeling fired up and ready to take your advocacy to the next level, why not dip your toes into broader advocacy activities? This could be anything from participating in mental health awareness campaigns, volunteering for organizations that support those with bipolar disorder, or even starting a blog or podcast. Every action, no matter how small, ripples outwards. It's about creating waves in the stagnant waters of stigma, showing that those with bipolar disorder aren't just surviving; they're thriving, leading, and changing the narrative.

We can shift perceptions by understanding stigma, harnessing the power of educated advocacy, carefully choosing words, and actively engaging in advocacy efforts. It's about painting a new picture, one where bipolar disorder is seen not just with understanding and empathy but as an integral part of the diverse human tapestry. Let's keep the conversation going, challenge the myths, and keep pushing for a world where no one has to whisper their diagnosis at a party—or anywhere else.

7.2 Educating Others: How to Share Your Story Effectively

When you decide to share your story of living with bipolar disorder, it's like deciding to let someone read a few pages of your diary. It's intimate, it's revealing, and yes, it can be a bit scary. However, the power of personal stories in breaking down barriers and fostering understanding cannot be overstated. Each time someone bravely shares their experience, the cloak of mystery that surrounds bipolar disorder gets a little lighter. It's about putting a human face on a condition often shrouded in myths and misconceptions, transforming abstract statistics into something palpable, honest, and relatable. Washington State has a group called "Stand up for Mental Health." It is a comedy group founded by David Granirer. From their website, it's a comedy therapy program teaching stand-up comedy to people with mental illness or mental health issues as a way of building confidence and fighting public stigma. You can read more at "http://standupformentalhealth.com/

"There are many ways to tell your story while helping yourself and others. Another source of reliable information is the National Alliance on Mental Illness (NAMI). You can read more about them at their website: https://www.nami.org/

Now, let's navigate the hows. Sharing your story is not just about what you say but how you say it, where you say it, and who you say it to. The platform you choose can make a big difference. Are you more comfortable writing a blog post, speaking at a community event, or perhaps sharing through a video on social media? Each medium reaches a different audience and comes with its own dynamic. For instance, writing gives you the time to choose your words carefully and to edit your thoughts for clarity and impact, while speaking directly to an audience can create an immediate, emotional connection that is both powerful and persuasive.

Setting boundaries is crucial for your emotional well-being. Before you share, decide how much you're comfortable revealing. It's okay not to divulge every detail; share what feels right for you. Consider preparing answers to potential questions from your audience, which can help steer the conversation toward areas you're comfortable discussing. And remember, you have the right to say, "I'd prefer not to go into detail about that." This protects you from feeling exposed or vulnerable beyond what you're prepared for.

Facing backlash is a reality for many who share their stories, especially on social media platforms where anonymity can embolden negativity. Prepare yourself for this possibility by bracing for it and cultivating a support network—friends, family, or a therapist—who can offer you a boost if things get tough. Focus on the positive impact your story may have. For every negative comment, there's a chance someone else feels seen, understood, or inspired to seek help because of your words. Keep your focus on these potential positives; let them be the wind in your sails against the rough waves of criticism.

Encouraging others to share their stories can multiply the impact of your advocacy. When one person speaks up, others are encouraged to do the same. If you can, foster an environment where sharing is supported and valued. This could be in a support group setting, through a blog or podcast, or at community events. Highlight the benefits of sharing—not just in educating others and reducing stigma but in personal empowerment and community building. Your story is a powerful beacon; it can light the way for others, showing them that they're not alone in their struggles and that their voices, too, have power.

In sharing your story, you're doing more than recounting events; you're changing the narrative around bipolar disorder, challenging stigma, and paving the way for a more understanding and supportive society. It's about turning your experiences into tools of education and instruments of change, and in doing so, you not only help others but also empower yourself. Through this act of bravery, you reclaim your narrative and remind us of the incredible resilience and diversity of the human spirit. So, share wisely, protect your peace, and remember that your story can enlighten, inspire, and transform, one word at a time.

7.3 Mental Health in the Workplace: Rights and Advocacy

Tiptoeing around the topic of bipolar disorder at work might feel like trying to dance ballet on a tightrope—high stakes, high stress, and a genuine fear of falling. But let's lace up those shoes and find a safer way to navigate workplace disclosure because, really, you deserve to work in an environment where you don't have to hide a part of who you are. Let's break down the intricacies of revealing your bipolar disorder at the office. Imagine this: You're armed with a toolkit, each tool representing a different aspect of the disclosure process. First up, timing—choosing when to disclose is like finding the right moment to jump into double Dutch. It's about finding that sweet spot where you feel secure in your role and trust the dynamics within your team.

Now, consider the pros and cons like you're weighing apples against oranges. On the one hand, disclosing can lead to accommodations that make your daily grind more manageable— think flexible hours or a quiet workspace away from the bustling open office. Conversely, there's always the risk of stigma, those old whispers of misunderstanding that might color colleagues' perceptions of your capabilities. It's a tough call, but knowledge is your safety net here. Understanding your company's policies on mental health can provide a solid foundation, showing you where and how the firm stands on supporting employees like you.

Rolling into the territory of legal rights feels like pulling on a superhero cape—suddenly, you're not just an employee but an employee backed by the law. In many regions, disability and employment laws, like the Americans with Disabilities Act (ADA) in the U.S., are there to protect you from discrimination. They ensure you can request reasonable accommodations without fear of retribution. But what does that look like in real life? It's not about dramatic gestures; it's the simple things like adjusting your work schedule to accommodate therapy sessions or even transitioning to a quieter part of the office to help you focus when you're navigating a depressive phase.

Advocating for mental health policies in your workplace can sometimes feel like you're trying to move a mountain. But remember, even mountains erode over time, especially when hit by the persistent flow of advocacy. Start small—maybe it's initiating a conversation with HR about mental health resources or organizing a workshop on mental health awareness. Every small action adds a layer to the foundation of a more understanding and supportive work environment. Think of it as planting seeds; with patience and care, these efforts can grow into a garden where diversity and mental wellness thrive.

Building this supportive environment doesn't require grand gestures. Sometimes, it's as simple as fostering open conversations about mental health or sharing resources and stories that humanize mental health challenges. It's about changing the narrative to move away from stigma and towards understanding and support. Consider this: if every workplace embraced even a fraction of these approaches, we could transform corporate cultures worldwide, making them bastions of support and understanding.

Navigating the complexities of mental health advocacy in the workplace is no small feat. Still, equipped with the proper knowledge, a clear understanding of your rights, and a strategy for advocacy, you can create waves of change, not just for yourself but for everyone who might feel like they're walking that tightrope alone. Let's keep pushing for workplaces that aren't just about productivity but also about people—where every employee has the support they need to survive and thrive.

7.4 Joining the Wider Conversation: Community and Advocacy

Imagine if every voice that ever felt stifled by the weight of bipolar disorder could join in a harmonious chorus, singing out not just for awareness but for action and change. That's the power of community involvement, a force that amplifies individual whispers into a roar that can't be ignored. When you step into the sphere of local and online bipolar disorder communities, you're not just entering a support group; you're stepping into a powerhouse of collective experience and advocacy. Here, every shared story, every exchanged tip, every word of encouragement acts like a thread, weaving a stronger safety net for all its members.

Now, think about this: each community event you participate in and each discussion you engage in adds momentum to the broader mission of destigmatizing bipolar disorder. It's like each of us holds a puzzle piece, and by coming together, we start seeing the complete picture, not just of the challenges but also of the potential for change. Local chapters of national mental health organizations often hold meetings, workshops, and public events. Getting involved in these activities allows you to connect with others navigating similar paths, perhaps in slightly different shoes. These interactions can be eye-opening, providing fresh perspectives and innovative approaches to managing bipolar disorder that you might not have considered before.

Shifting gears, let's talk about the digital age's superpower—social media. It's a tool that can broadcast your voice far beyond your local community, reaching across cities, countries, and continents. When used effectively, social media platforms become stages for advocacy and awareness, where your experiences and insights can touch lives in places you've never been. Here's the trick: maintaining a balance between being open and protecting your privacy is crucial. Deciding how much or little you want to share is perfectly okay. The goal is to foster understanding and support, not to overshare to the point where you feel exposed. You might consider using platforms that allow you to control who sees your posts or create content that focuses on general education and awareness. Keep your details vague but your message clear.

Collaborating with mental health organizations can significantly boost your advocacy efforts. These organizations often have the resources, networks, and platforms to help propel your message to a broader audience. These collaborations can be mutually beneficial if you contribute to their blogs, speak at their events, or even lead a workshop. You bring authentic, personal experience to the table, which enriches their programs and makes their outreach more relatable and impactful.

Now, let's widen the lens even further and consider the global and cultural perspectives on bipolar disorder. This disorder does not recognize borders or cultural lines; it is a universal human experience that varies only in how different cultures understand and address it. By learning about and integrating these diverse perspectives into your advocacy efforts, you're broadening your understanding and enriching the global dialogue on mental health. It helps to remember that in some cultures, mental health may still be a taboo subject, where discussions might be more restrained and require a sensitive approach. Being aware of and respectful of these differences can make your advocacy more inclusive and effective.

Engaging in these broader conversations about bipolar disorder and mental health not only strengthens your support network but also contributes to a more significant movement toward acceptance and change. It's about building bridges, opening dialogues, and ensuring the conversation around bipolar disorder is inclusive, informed, and impactful. By joining this more comprehensive conversation, you help ensure that the future of mental health advocacy is vibrant, diverse, and rich with the voices of those who live with these experiences every day. Let's keep the conversation growing louder and more inclusive with each new voice joining in.

7.5 Using Social Media for Support and Awareness

Ah, social media—where else can you find cat videos, culinary masterpieces, and meaningful mental health support all in the same place? It's a landscape where hashtags can start movements, and a single post can echo through the lives of thousands. For those navigating the waves of bipolar disorder, social media offers both a beacon of support and a platform for advocacy. But, as with any powerful tool, the key lies in using it wisely and well.

The Role of Social Media

Think of social media as a global coffee shop where conversations about mental health can happen openly and honestly. It's transformed from just a place to share selfies and gourmet meals to a significant arena for mental health discourse, providing those with conditions like bipolar disorder a space to connect, learn, and feel less alone. For instance, hashtags like #BipolarDisorder or #MentalHealthAwareness can lead you to a treasure trove of stories, advice, and support from all corners of the globe. It's about turning isolation into community, giving you a sense of solidarity that can be hard to find offline.

Social media also serves as a critical platform for raising public awareness about bipolar disorder. Through campaigns, shared articles, and personal stories, it can educate a broad audience about the realities of living with bipolar disorder, chipping away at the stigma. Each shared experience helps paint a more comprehensive, more nuanced picture of what bipolar disorder really looks like, breaking down misconceptions and fostering a more informed public dialogue. It's like each post, each tweet and each story is a brushstroke in a much larger mural depicting the true face of mental health.

Creating Engaging Content

Creating content that resonates and educates isn't just about pouring your heart out on the keyboard. It's about crafting your message in a way that engages and informs. Start with authenticity—be true to your experiences and feelings. Authenticity resonates; it cuts through social media noise like a bell. Combine this with educational tidbits, like quick facts about bipolar disorder or debunking myths. Imagine you're creating a mini-infographic in each post. For example, a simple, eye-catching image paired with a caption, "Did you know bipolar disorder affects over 5 million adults in the U.S. alone? Let's talk about it!" can grab attention and spread knowledge.

But let's spice it up a bit. Humor, when appropriate, can be a powerful tool. A light-hearted meme about the ups and downs of bipolar disorder can not only bring a smile but also make a point in a relatable way. Visual content, like videos or themed photo series, can boost engagement. Maybe it's a video diary of a week in your life with bipolar disorder or a series of portraits of individuals thriving despite their diagnosis—visual stories that invite viewers into your world.

Navigating Online Communities

Finding the right online community is like finding the right coffee shop. You want a place where you feel comfortable, where the vibe is supportive, and where the baristas (or moderators, in this case) ensure a safe, welcoming environment. Start by exploring groups focused on mental health, particularly those that cater to bipolar disorder. Read the posts, check the interactions, and understand the community's tone and rules.

Once you've found a community that feels like a good fit, jump in—but remember, it's about both giving and taking. Share your experiences and support, and seek advice and camaraderie when needed. Engage respectfully, remembering that every member is navigating their challenges. This give-and-take strengthens the fabric of these communities, weaving a network of support that extends far beyond the screen.

Digital Self-Care

But here's the thing—while social media can be a lifeline, it can also be a whirlpool, pulling you into depths of negativity or oversharing. That's where digital self-care comes into play. It's about setting boundaries for how much time you spend online and being mindful of how this time affects your mood. Notice when exposure to certain content triggers negative feelings or exacerbates your symptoms. When this happens, give yourself permission to step back, unfollow, or mute accounts that impact your mental health negatively.

Take regular breaks. Like any space, social media can feel overwhelming. Schedule 'offline' periods into your day to disconnect from the digital world and reconnect with the physical one. Go for a walk, meditate, or bask in a few quiet moments—whatever helps you reset. Remember, the online world will still be there when you return, but your well-being must come first.

Navigating social media as someone with bipolar disorder means balancing its benefits with its challenges. By understanding its role, creating engaging and authentic content, actively participating in supportive communities, and practicing diligent digital self-care, you harness this modern tool for support, education, and connection, turning what could be a battleground into a haven. In this place, understanding and community flourish.

7.6 The Power of Peer Support: Finding and Offering Help

Imagine walking into a room where everyone speaks your language, not just linguistically but emotionally and experientially. That's what a good peer support group feels like for someone with bipolar disorder. It's a place where the walls come down, you can share without fear of judgment, and the nods of understanding are as comforting as a cozy blanket on a chilly evening. Peer support groups provide a unique blend of empathy, shared experiences, and collective wisdom that can be a lifeline in managing the complexities of bipolar disorder.

The beauty of peer support lies in its foundation of mutual understanding. Here, you're not just receiving support; you're surrounded by individuals who get the highs and lows because they've ridden similar roller-coasters. This environment fosters a deep sense of community and belonging, which can be incredibly validating when you feel isolated by your condition. The shared stories and strategies can also be enlightening, offering new perspectives and coping mechanisms that might not have crossed your radar otherwise. It's like having a living library at your fingertips, where the books breathe and speak, each one offering insights into different chapters of managing bipolar disorder.

But how do you find the right group? It's a bit like dating—you might need to meet a few before you find the one that clicks. Start by searching for local support groups in your community. Hospitals, mental health clinics, and organizations dedicated to bipolar disorder often host or direct you to existing groups. Online platforms can also be goldmines for peer support. Websites devoted to mental health and social media groups offer virtual communities that can be accessed from the comfort of your home. When selecting a group, consider the format—is it a formal meeting with a facilitator or a more casual meet-up? What's the group's policy on confidentiality, and how do they ensure a safe and supportive environment? Answering these questions can help gauge whether the group's vibe aligns with your needs and comfort level.

Transitioning from a group member to a peer supporter can be rewarding. If you find yourself drawn to the idea of guiding and supporting others through their bipolar experiences, becoming a peer supporter might be a natural next step. This role often requires some training, which many organizations provide. Training programs typically cover vital skills such as active listening, confidentiality, crisis response, and boundary-setting, preparing you to facilitate sessions effectively and empathetically. The personal benefits of this role are profound; it's not just about giving back but also about strengthening your coping strategies and resilience. Teaching is often the best way to understand a subject deeply, and by articulating and advising on coping mechanisms, you reinforce these practices in your own life.

However, as you step into a support role, remember the golden rule of peer support: boundaries. Maintaining clear boundaries ensures that your support role remains healthy and doesn't infringe on your well-being or group dynamics. It's essential to recognize the limits of your role—you're there to support, not to treat or counsel. This distinction helps prevent burnout and ensures that your involvement remains a positive force in your life and those you support.

Peer support is an invaluable facet of living with and managing bipolar disorder. It provides a platform for emotional support, personal growth, and empowerment. Whether as a member or a supporter, participating in these groups contributes to a vibrant community that thrives on shared strength and understanding. Each meeting, each story, and each shared struggle and triumph weave a more robust, supportive tapestry for everyone involved.

As we close this chapter on peer support, let's reflect on the power of shared experiences and the profound impact of empathy and understanding in managing bipolar disorder. We find both help and hope through peer support—strategies and strength. These connections remind us that we do not travel alone while our journeys are personal. Let's carry this spirit of community and support forward as we continue to explore ways to live fully and vibrantly with bipolar disorder.

CHAPTER:8
LONG-TERM MANAGEMENT
AND FUTURE PLANNING

Picture this: You've just built a spectacular sandcastle, complete with towers, a moat, and even a tiny flag on top. Now, imagine the tide is coming in. You wouldn't just leave your masterpiece to the mercy of the waves, right? You'd probably start reinforcing the walls, maybe building a barrier or two. That's a bit like managing bipolar disorder in the long run. It's about building resilience and preparing for the ebbs and flows, ensuring your hard work—your stability, your mental peace—stays intact, even when the tides of life get a little rough.

8.1 Building Resilience: Strategies for Long-Term Stability

Understanding Resilience

Let's kick off with a clear picture of what resilience means in the context of bipolar disorder. Think of resilience as your psychological immune system, a built-in buffer against the stressors and storms of life. It's not about avoiding episodes or never facing challenges—that's about as realistic as wearing bubble wrap to avoid getting bumped. Instead, resilience is about bouncing back. It's about having the tools and the toughness to get up when knocked down and learn from each experience so you're even stronger for the next round.

For anyone living with bipolar disorder, resilience is a key player. It's what turns "I can't handle this" into "I've got this." It's the difference between a setback defining your path or refining it. Building resilience means equipping yourself with strategies to navigate manic and depressive episodes and integrating practices into your life that promote long-term stability. It's about crafting a life that withstands the waves and learns to surf them.

Developing Coping Skills

Now, let's dive into the nitty-gritty of developing the coping skills that build resilience. First up is problem-solving. Life throws curveballs, and bipolar disorder might add some spin. Developing strong problem-solving skills means getting better at identifying problems (like recognizing the onset of a mood swing), brainstorming potential solutions (maybe adjusting your sleep schedule or medication), and implementing these solutions before things escalate.

Next, we have emotional regulation. It's all about managing those intense emotions without letting them tip you over. Techniques like mindfulness, deep breathing, or expressive writing can help keep your emotional boat steady in choppy waters. It's like installing a set of emotional shock absorbers ready to smooth out the jolts.

Of course, there's seeking support. Whether from friends, family, a therapist, or a support group, building a network of people who get it and have your back can make all the difference. It's like having a team in your corner, ready to pass you water and a towel and to cheer you on every step of the way.

Creating a Support System

Speaking of support, let's talk about how to build that dream team. A robust support system is more than just having people around; it's about having the right people around. Family and friends who are educated about bipolar disorder can provide not just companionship but also understanding and practical help. Healthcare providers, from your psychiatrist to your therapist, are your professional support squad, crucial for managing the clinical aspects of bipolar disorder.

But don't forget about peer support. Connecting with others walking a similar path can provide insights and empathy you might not find elsewhere. They're the ones who can say, "Me too," and mean it, who can share strategies that worked (or didn't), and who can truly understand the ups and downs you're experiencing.

Stress Management and Mindfulness

Last but not least, let's tackle stress management and mindfulness. If stress is like wind to a wildfire, then learning to manage it is crucial. Techniques like mindfulness can help you stay present and grounded, reducing overall stress and helping to mitigate triggers that might lead to mood episodes. Consider mindfulness as your mental pause button, allowing you to stop, breathe, and respond to situations more clearly rather than in haste.

Incorporating regular mindfulness practices, such as meditation, yoga, or even mindful walking, can significantly enhance your resilience. It's about creating a calm core amid life's chaos, a center from which you can operate with peace and perspective. And when the winds do pick up, you'll be ready to withstand them but to harness them, turning challenges into opportunities for growth and learning.

8.2 Anticipating and Managing Bipolar Episodes

Let's imagine for a moment that you're the captain of a ship. Navigating the ocean is like managing bipolar disorder: calm seas can turn stormy in a flash, and you might struggle to stay afloat without a good map and a solid plan. Learning to recognize the early warning signs of your bipolar episodes is akin to spotting those dark clouds on the horizon—it's your first clue that you need to prepare for rough weather. These signs can be subtle, like feeling just a bit too energetic or finding that your thoughts start racing like a sports car at a green light. Or maybe it's the opposite; things start slowing down, and getting out of bed feels as rigid as swimming through syrup.

Now, once you've spotted these signs, what's next? This is where your action plans come into play. Think of them as your navigation charts, guiding you safely through the storm. Crafting a personalized action plan involves mapping out what steps to take when symptoms begin to amplify. This might include adjusting your medication under medical guidance, scheduling extra therapy sessions, or temporarily tweaking your daily routines to reduce stress. It's about having a clear, concrete plan to act when you see those warning signs rather than waiting for the storm to hit in full force.

Engaging your support network effectively is crucial and can be delicate. Your loved ones must know what to expect and how they can assist. This isn't about them taking control but about offering support in ways that truly help. Whether giving you space when you need it, providing a listening ear, or ensuring you don't miss a medication dose, their informed, sensitive involvement can be a lifeline during turbulent times. It's about them understanding your condition well enough to offer the right kind of support at the right time, which requires open, ongoing communication. Let them know what works and what doesn't, and remember, this is a two-way street; they need your guidance as much as you need their support.

Managing medication over the long haul is another critical aspect of navigating bipolar disorder. Medications can change in effectiveness over time, and side effects can evolve. It's like maintaining your ship; it requires regular check-ups and tune-ups. Staying in close communication with your healthcare provider about how your medications affect you is essential. Sometimes, minor adjustments can significantly affect how you feel and function. It's also important to keep track of any new symptoms or changes in your health, as they can be clues that your medication needs reevaluation. Remember, this is a marathon, not a sprint, and maintaining stability often means being proactive about your treatment plan, always with the guidance of your healthcare professionals.

By recognizing early signs, having robust action plans, wisely involving your loved ones, and managing your medication effectively, you're not just reacting to the storm—you're skillfully navigating through it, keeping your ship steady and your journey on course.

8.3 The Role of Routine Medical Care in Bipolar Management

Imagine treating your bipolar disorder management like you would a high-stakes game of chess. Each piece, from your daily routines to your coping strategies, plays a crucial role. But let's not forget the king on this chessboard: routine medical care. Regular check-ups with your mental health professionals are akin to making strategic moves that keep you safe and checkmate the disorder before it can declare a victory. These appointments allow you to review your treatment progress, make necessary tweaks, and ensure everything is on track. Just like a chess master reviews past games, these sessions help you and your healthcare provider analyze what's working and what isn't, ensuring that your treatment strategy evolves as you do.

Building a collaborative relationship with your healthcare providers is like forming a dynamic duo. It's about more than just showing up; it's about engaging actively in your treatment plan. Good communication is the cornerstone here. It means being open about your feelings, asking questions, and expressing concerns about your treatment. Think of it as having a co-pilot; while in the driver's seat, your healthcare provider is there to help navigate, offering expert advice and ensuring you don't miss any turns. It can be helpful to come prepared with notes or a list of topics you want to discuss, making the most of your time during each visit. And remember, setting mutual goals during these appointments can give you clear markers of progress and success, which can be incredibly motivating as you manage your bipolar disorder.

Now, let's talk about the physical aspect of things. Monitoring and managing physical health issues that arise as side effects of bipolar disorder or its treatments are as crucial as mental management itself. Some medications might have side effects that affect your physical health, such as weight gain, sleep disturbances, or more complex metabolic changes. Regular physical check-ups, therefore, are as non-negotiable as your psychiatric evaluations. These help catch potential issues early, allowing for adjustments before they become problematic. It's like watching all parts of the engine, not just the one making the most noise.

Maintaining your mental health over the long term is an ongoing process, a continuous commitment to self-care practices, therapy, and peer support. It's about finding a rhythm in therapy sessions, perhaps discovering new coping mechanisms or exploring deeper issues that influence your condition. Peer support groups can also provide a sense of community and belonging, offering practical advice and emotional solace. Self-care practices, whether regular exercise, mindfulness meditation, or journaling, act as daily maintenance for your mental well-being, like oiling the gears of a well-used machine to keep it running smoothly.

In this ongoing game of chess, where bipolar disorder brings unexpected moves, routine medical care, collaborative relationships with healthcare providers, vigilant physical health monitoring, and steadfast mental health maintenance are your best strategies for a checkmate. By staying committed to these aspects, you ensure that your management plan is as dynamic and resilient as you are, ready to adapt and respond to whatever comes your way.

8.4 Estate and Financial Planning: Preparing for the Future

Let's talk money and future planning—two things that might not be as exciting as planning your next vacation, but trust me, they're just as important. Managing finances and planning your estate when you have bipolar disorder is a bit like being a circus ringmaster. You've got to watch all the acts, from the high-flying trapeze of investments to the juggling act of savings and the tightrope walk of budgeting. It's thrilling in its own way, especially when you get everything to work in harmony. So, let's pull back the curtain on managing this financial circus with flair and foresight.

First, achieving and maintaining financial stability is your main act. It starts with the cornerstone of any sound financial plan: budgeting. Crafting a budget isn't about restricting yourself; it's about understanding your financial flow, much like a choreographer plans out dance moves. You need to know where every dollar is going, especially since mood swings can sometimes lead to impulsive spending. Start with tracking your income and expenses. Use apps or good old spreadsheets—whatever floats your boat. See where you can cut back without cutting out joy. Remember, a good budget flexes with you, giving you room to breathe and adapt.

Now, onto saving and investing, which can be your safety net. Consider saving as packing a parachute; you hope not to need it, but it's there to save the day if you do. Start small if you have to. A little can go a long way, especially with compound interest. As for investing, it's like planting a garden. It takes patience and a bit of risk tolerance, but the payoff can be well worth it. Consider talking to a financial advisor who understands the nuances of investing while managing a condition like bipolar disorder. They can help tailor an investment strategy that matches your risk tolerance and long-term goals.

Transitioning to estate planning, this is where you get to direct how the show goes on, even if you're not around to see it. It's about making sure your assets are distributed according to your wishes and that decisions about your health and finances can be made by someone you trust if you cannot do so. Start with the basics: a will, like your script, telling everyone what you want to happen. Then, consider setting up a power of attorney and a healthcare directive. These are your backstage crew, ready to step in and ensure your wishes are respected when you can't call the shots.

Navigating insurance and planning for future care needs might not be glamorous, but it's critical. Consider insurance as your contingency plan; the understudy is ready to step in when needed. Whether it's health insurance to cover therapy sessions and medication or long-term disability insurance just in case, being covered provides peace of mind. As for future care planning, it's about looking ahead. If your condition might require long-term treatment or care, planning now can make a world of difference later. Look into long-term care options and ensure your insurance can cover the kind of care you envision for yourself.

Lastly, let's spotlight some resources and professional assistance. Managing finances and planning for the future isn't a solo act. Some professionals specialize in helping individuals with chronic conditions manage their money and plan their estates. Organizations like the National Disability Institute offer financial planning resources sensitive to the needs of those with chronic conditions. Financial advisors specializing in estate planning can also provide invaluable guidance, ensuring your financial plans are as robust as possible.

Navigating your financial future when you have bipolar disorder doesn't have to be a high-wire act performed without a net. With careful planning, a good support team, and the right tools and knowledge, you can create a financial plan that meets your needs and gives you the confidence to enjoy the present, knowing the future is well-handled. So, please take a deep breath, and let's get this show on the road. Your future self will thank you for it.

8.5 Career Planning and Bipolar: Navigating Success and Challenges

Handling a career while managing bipolar disorder is akin to sailing a ship through unpredictable seas—you need a well-calibrated compass, a precise map, and the flexibility to adjust your sails as conditions change. Setting realistic and fulfilling career goals is your compass here. It's about aligning your professional aspirations with the realities of your condition, ensuring that your career path brings satisfaction and accommodates your health needs. Think about what success means to you. Is it climbing the corporate ladder or achieving a balanced life where work is just one part of your happiness equation? Understanding your true north will guide every decision, from job choices to daily tasks.

When it comes to workplace disclosure, imagine standing at a crossroads where one path is open about your bipolar disorder, and the other is more private. Each has pros and cons; the correct path depends on your unique situation and work environment. Disclosing can open the door to support and accommodations, such as flexible working hours or a quiet workspace. However, it also involves a certain level of vulnerability, as biases and misunderstandings about bipolar disorder still exist in many workplaces. Gauge your organization's culture—are mental health matters handled with sensitivity and discretion? Your answer might determine whether you share your diagnosis or choose to keep it private. If you decide to disclose, timing is crucial; it's often best after establishing your capabilities and building a rapport with your team.

Achieving professional success involves leveraging your strengths—those unique superpowers that bipolar disorder can't touch. Maybe it's your creativity, your ability to think outside the box or your resilience. Play to these strengths. Look for roles that not only require these skills but also celebrate them. Managing stress is also part of this equation. It's like knowing when to take your foot off the accelerator at work to prevent burnout. Develop strategies such as prioritizing tasks, setting clear boundaries between work and home life, and using relaxation techniques to manage stress effectively. Additionally, utilizing workplace accommodations can be a game-changer. Whether it's a flexible schedule that aligns with your energy patterns or the ability to work from home during depressive phases, these accommodations can help you maintain stability and optimize your performance.

Now, what about those considering a career change? This can feel like rewiring your entire professional existence, but sometimes, aligning more closely with your strengths and health needs is necessary. Start by evaluating what's missing in your current role. Is it creativity, flexibility, or perhaps a supportive environment? Then, look at career paths that not only interest you but also offer the accommodations you need to manage your bipolar disorder effectively. Research is fundamental—talk to people in those fields, look up job satisfaction rates, and consider the day-to-day responsibilities. It's about finding a fit that feels as right in practice as it does on paper. As you consider this change, think about the long-term management of your disorder. Will this new path provide enough stability and support? How will it impact your routine and treatment regimen? These considerations are crucial to ensure that your career change is not just a leap in the dark but a well-informed step into a more fulfilling professional life.

Directing your career while managing bipolar disorder requires a blend of self-awareness, strategic planning, and proactive adaptation. By setting clear, realistic goals, carefully considering disclosure, leveraging your strengths, managing stress, and thoughtfully considering career changes, you create a professional life that meets your aspirations and supports your well-being. This approach allows you to survive in your career and thrive, turning challenges into opportunities and your condition into a portal for unique professional contributions.

8.6 New and Emerging Treatments: Staying Informed

Staying on top of the latest trends can sometimes feel like trying to sip from a fire hose—overwhelming. But when it comes to managing bipolar disorder, keeping up with new research and treatments isn't just valuable; it's crucial. Think of it as staying ahead in a game where the rules keep evolving. The landscape of bipolar disorder treatment is continually advancing, with fresh studies, innovative therapies, and groundbreaking technologies emerging at a pace that can be hard to keep up with, yet incredibly exciting.

First, understanding the importance of staying informed about new research and treatments for bipolar disorder is akin to knowing the weather forecast before planning a picnic. It prepares you for what's coming, helps you make informed decisions, and ensures you utilize the best tools to manage your condition effectively. New research can offer insights into better management strategies, more effective medications, or even lifestyle changes that could significantly impact your quality of life. It's about giving yourself every possible advantage in managing your health.

Let's talk about evaluating these new treatments. Not all that glitters is gold. When you come across a new treatment or therapy option, it's essential to vet its credibility and potential impact thoroughly. Start by checking if the findings are from a reputable source, such as a well-respected medical journal or a leading bipolar disorder research organization. Look into who conducted the study—consider their credentials and any potential biases they might have. Also, the size and scope of the study should be evaluated; more extensive, more diverse study populations often provide more reliable insights. Discuss these treatments with your healthcare provider to understand how they might fit into your existing management plan. Considering your specific circumstances, they can help you weigh the benefits against the risks.

Participating in clinical trials is another avenue that can be both intriguing and intimidating. Clinical trials for new bipolar treatments provide a firsthand look at up-and-coming therapies and medications. However, they're a mixed bag of potential and precaution. Additionally, participating in a clinical trial can give you access to new treatments before they are widely available. It's a chance to be on the cutting edge of science, contributing to research that might change lives, possibly even your own. On the flip side, there are risks. New treatments can have unforeseen side effects or be less effective than hoped. If you're considering a clinical trial, start by thoroughly researching the trial's scope, the treatments involved, and the institution conducting the trial. Ensure the trial is registered with a recognized medical authority and understand all the consent forms before signing on the dotted line.

Lastly, let's dive into the exciting world of technology and therapy advances. Digital tools like mood-tracking apps and teletherapy are revolutionizing how bipolar disorder is managed. Mood-tracking apps, for instance, help you monitor your emotional landscape, giving you and your healthcare provider valuable data to understand better and manage your condition. Conversely, teletherapy breaks down geographical and logistical barriers, providing access to mental health support from the comfort of your home. These technological advancements are about convenience and making comprehensive, continuous care more accessible and practical.

As we wrap up this exploration of new and emerging treatments, remember that being well-informed is your best defense in the dynamic battlefield of bipolar disorder management. It empowers you to make educated decisions about your health care, keeps you connected to the latest advancements, and ultimately supports your journey toward stability and wellness. As we look forward to the next chapter, let's carry this mindset of informed curiosity and proactive engagement, continuing to explore ways to enhance our lives despite the challenges posed by bipolar disorder.

CHAPTER:9
PERSONAL GROWTH AND TRANSFORMATION

Imagine if someone told you that the very traits attributed to your bipolar disorder could be your greatest assets. It sounds like being told your worst Monday could somehow turn into your best Saturday, right? But here's the kicker—it's true. Living with bipolar disorder molds resilience, sharpens creativity, and sculpts a unique perspective on the world that can be as valuable as any masterpiece in a gallery.

9.1 Harnessing Your Bipolar Superpowers: Creativity and Resilience

Identifying Personal Strengths

Think of your journey with bipolar disorder as an intense training program you never signed up for. Sure, it's tough. It throws a curve ball faster than a major league pitcher but also builds some serious muscle in areas of your life that others might overlook. Let's start with identifying these strengths. You've probably developed a high level of empathy, a keen sense of self-awareness, or perhaps an ability to think outside the box—highly prized qualities in many areas of life and work.

Take a moment to reflect on the times when your unique traits positively impacted your life or the lives of others. Maybe it's your empathetic nature that has deepened your relationships or your creative thinking that has solved problems at work in ways nobody else could fathom. Recognizing and embracing these strengths isn't just about feeling good about yourself—it's about structuring your life around these powers. It's like realizing you've been sitting on a pile of gold. So dig in, discover these nuggets, and put them to work.

Creativity as an Outlet

Now, about that creativity—bipolar disorder and creativity have been linked in studies and anecdotes alike, suggesting that the same fire that fuels the emotional extremes of bipolar disorder may also ignite some extraordinary creative sparks. Historical figures like Virginia Woolf and modern icons like Carrie Fisher have all channeled their tumultuous energies into creating impactful art and literature, turning their experiences with bipolar disorder into powerful expressions of human emotion.

But here's the truly remarkable part—you don't need to be a famous artist to harness this aspect of bipolar disorder. Creativity comes in countless forms, from painting and writing to cooking, gardening, coding, or even devising new ways to organize your space. Whatever form it takes for you, creativity is not just an outlet for expression; it's a form of therapy. It's a way to externalize feelings, to play with them, and to see them in a different light. So, pick up that paintbrush, spatula, or spreadsheet—whatever tools you need to transform your experiences into something uniquely yours.

Building Resilience

Building resilience might sound like one of those easier-said-than-done tasks, and in some ways, it is. It's an ongoing process, like sculpting, chipping away at the not-so-great bits to reveal a more robust and defined figure beneath. Each challenge faced and navigated in the realm of bipolar disorder serves as a chisel, defining your resilience. Strategies here are about proactive management and reactive grace under pressure—maintaining treatment, yes, but also developing coping strategies that allow you to meet and greet your challenges head-on.

This might mean setting up a daily routine that includes relaxation and mindfulness or establishing a regular check-in with yourself to assess your mental landscape. Think of resilience not just as bouncing back but as bouncing forward—using the energy from each fall to propel you into a better, stronger position.

Celebrating Uniqueness

Finally, let's talk about celebrating your uniqueness. Living with bipolar disorder can sometimes feel like you're constantly being told how different you are, and not always in a good way. But here's a radical thought: what if those differences are your superpowers? What if the very qualities that make you 'different' are what make you extraordinary?

Embrace your unique perspective on the world—it's a view that can inspire, enlighten, and even change the minds and hearts of those around you. Celebrate your ability to feel deeply, to think widely, and to choose bravely. Own your story, insights, creativity, and resilience as badges of honor. Not only do they make you who you are, but they also equip you to contribute to the world in ways no one else can.

In this chapter, we've unpacked just a few of the superpowers often accompanying bipolar disorder—creativity, resilience, and a unique perspective. As you continue to navigate your path, remember that these traits are not just byproducts of your experiences with bipolar disorder; they are integral parts of the incredible, multifaceted person you are. Celebrate them, use them, and watch how they transform not just your life but also the lives of those around you.

9.2 Bipolar Disorder and Identity: A Journey of Self-Discovery

Imagine waking up one day to find you've been wearing a slightly incorrect name tag. It's not entirely wrong, but it certainly doesn't capture everything about who you are. That's a bit like what it feels like to be defined by a bipolar diagnosis. Sure, it's one aspect of your identity, but it's not the whole story. There's an entire landscape of your personality to explore beyond the borders of bipolar disorder, and it's rich with features shaped by more than just your mental health status.

Exploring your identity beyond bipolar disorder is like setting out on a grand expedition where the goal is not to find new lands but to understand the contours of your terrain. It involves peeling back the layers of labels that life and circumstances have stuck on you and getting to the rock-solid core of your personal values, interests, and aspirations. Start by asking yourself what makes you feel alive, independent of your mental health. Is it the quiet satisfaction of reading a good book? The thrill of hiking up a challenging trail? Or the joy of a perfectly baked pie? These passions and pursuits are integral colors in the tapestry of your identity. They provide a counterbalance to the weight of a bipolar diagnosis, reminding you and the world that your identity is a spectrum of experiences, talents, and dreams.

Now, let's talk about forging a positive self-image. It's easy to fall into a whirlpool of negative self-talk, especially when you're dealing with the highs and lows of bipolar disorder. But think of your mind as a garden. Negative thoughts are like weeds that can overrun it if left unchecked. Cultivating a positive self-image starts with pulling out these weeds and planting seeds of positive affirmations in their place. Celebrate your victories, no matter how small. Have you finished a project at work? That's a win. Manage to meet a friend for coffee during a low week? Another win. These achievements, minor as they might seem, are affirmations of your capabilities and worth. Make a habit of acknowledging them. Write them down, talk about them, or take a moment to appreciate them internally. Each acknowledgment fertilizes the soil of your self-esteem, gradually growing a garden where your worth is defined by more than the shadows of bipolar disorder.

Living with bipolar disorder inevitably sculpts your character in unique ways. It teaches you empathy as you understand what it means to face struggles that are not immediately visible. It teaches you patience with yourself and others as you navigate the unpredictability of mood swings. And importantly, it builds resilience as you learn to rise, again and again, embracing both your vulnerabilities and your strengths. These qualities are not just silver linings but integral components of personal growth. They are forged in the fire of managing bipolar disorder and emerge as tools to help you connect with others, overcome challenges, and pursue your life goals with a deepened understanding of human experience.

Lastly, narrative therapy and personal storytelling are powerful tools for exploring and affirming your identity. This approach involves framing your life experiences as stories, with you as the narrator and the protagonist. Crafting your narrative can be incredibly empowering. It allows you to tell your story on your terms, to highlight the battles you've won and the lessons you've learned. It's about taking control of the narrative thread and weaving a story that acknowledges bipolar disorder as part of your plot but not the entirety of it. By doing so, you reclaim your identity from the clutches of stigma and redefine it to reflect your true self, with all its complexities and colors.   Whether through writing, art, or speaking, engaging in narrative therapy helps you externalize your experiences, making it easier to see how far you've come and where you want to go next. It's not just about recounting past events; it's about scripting a future where you are the hero of your own story, equipped with a deeper understanding of your strengths and how you can use them to navigate the chapters yet to come.

9.3 From Surviving to Thriving: Real-Life Success Stories

Let's shift gears and tap into some truly motivating tales from the real world—stories of individuals who didn't just handle their bipolar disorder; they thrived because of and despite it. These narratives aren't just feel-good moments but profound lessons in perseverance, understanding, and personal triumph. Picture this: each story is a beacon, lighting up paths you might walk down, showing that the hurdles of bipolar disorder don't have to be roadblocks; they can be stepping stones to something greater.

Take, for instance, the story of Alex, a graphic designer who once saw his intense mood swings as a barrier to success in the fast-paced, highly competitive creative industry. Alex struggled initially, finding the workplace environment and the pressure to consistently perform creatively during depressive episodes overwhelming. However, his journey took a turn when he began to channel his emotional highs and lows into his creative process, using periods of mania to fuel bold, innovative designs and times of depression to deepen his work's emotional impact. His unique approach not only brought him accolades in his field but also helped his colleagues and clients appreciate the depth and authenticity of his work. The key lesson here? Alex's success came from embracing his emotional experiences as assets rather than obstacles, transforming his workflow to align with the rhythms of his mood cycles.

Then there's Jenna, a social worker whose own experiences with bipolar disorder deeply enriched her ability to empathize with her clients. Jenna's diagnosis initially felt like a stigma that might hinder her career in mental health. Yet, it became clear that her insights into mental illness were invaluable. She could connect with her clients on a level that went beyond academic knowledge or professional training; she offered understanding rooted in lived experience. By openly discussing her challenges and victories in managing bipolar disorder, Jenna not only destigmatized her condition but also inspired her clients to be more open about their struggles. Her story underscores the importance of vulnerability and authenticity in transforming personal challenges into professional strengths, fostering an environment where mental health is openly discussed and managed without shame.

In case you are curious, after 30-plus years, I finally consider myself a success only recently. After many trials and errors, I have a medication cocktail that keeps me level and functioning. I spent a long time unmedicated while in the military. I burned many bridges and made lots of bad decisions. In the end, I was medically retired for other issues. Imagine not having the internet or the wealth of information that is now available. Everyone thought I was a ticking bomb! Without knowing the reason for my behavior. I won't sit here and narrate my whole string of failures, but trust me when I say I'm textbook. Thanks to newer drugs and therapy, I can see the patterns and prepare to preempt my illness before I can make any decisions that would have lasting consequences. I journal a lot, have been trying my hand at creating art, do Pilates, and practice mindfulness these days. It's a work in progress.

Reflecting on these stories, it's evident that thriving with bipolar disorder often involves redefining success. It's about recognizing that the journey is as unique as the individual and that success may not always fit into a conventional mold. This perspective is crucial because it celebrates diversity in paths to fulfillment and achievement, acknowledging that everyone's best looks different.

Encouragement to chase after your dreams—even when the path is unpredictable and the outcomes uncertain—is a theme that resonates deeply in these stories. Consider Mark, a teacher who dreamed of starting his own school. The fluctuating energy levels and unpredictable mood swings caused by his bipolar disorder made the immense task seem daunting. However, Mark's passion for education and desire to create an inclusive learning environment drove him to pursue his dream. He learned to delegate tasks during low-energy days and capitalize on his bursts of manic energy to fuel planning and creative problem-solving. Mark's school is now a reality, providing a supportive, adaptive learning environment that caters to students with diverse needs. His experience highlights the importance of adaptability and resilience, showing that you can turn your aspirations into achievements with the right strategies and support, regardless of the hurdles you might face.

These stories, each rich with struggle, triumph, and wisdom, serve as powerful reminders of the resilience and potential of individuals navigating life with bipolar disorder. They teach us that with understanding, support, and a willingness to adapt, thriving is not just a possibility but a probable outcome. Let these narratives inspire you to look at your challenges through a lens of opportunity, reframe obstacles as growth catalysts, and pursue your dreams with renewed vigor and hope, knowing that your unique journey can lead to unexpected and fulfilling destinations.

9.4 The Positive Impact of Bipolar on Personal Relationships

Let's chat about relationships. Not just any relationships but those that blossom in the garden you've cultivated through your experiences with bipolar disorder. It might seem like a stretch to view this condition as a cultivator of more profound, meaningful connections, but stay with me here—it truly can be.

Deepening Relationships Through Vulnerability

Picture this: you're standing at the edge of a diving board—the high one. Below, your friends are treading water, looking up, encouraging you to jump. Sharing your experiences with bipolar disorder with someone is like taking that leap. It's terrifying, but it's also an incredible display of trust. And just like diving into that pool, opening up can strengthen your bonds with those around you in ways you might not expect. When you share your story, you're not just sharing the highs and lows; you're inviting someone into your inner world, giving them a backstage pass to the workings of your mind. This vulnerability can transform relationships, turning casual connections into profound sources of mutual support and understanding.

This kind of sharing does more than deepen existing bonds; it can also filter out relationships that might not be suited to withstand the complexities of your life. Think of it as relationship triage, where the strength of each bond is tested. Those who stay, listen, and support you offer a foundation of trust and empathy on which you can build a lasting and resilient relationship.

Empathy and Understanding

Living with bipolar disorder naturally cultivates a profound sense of empathy. You know what it's like to feel misunderstood, to struggle silently, or to face challenges that aren't visible to the naked eye. This can make you incredibly attuned to the struggles of others, often seeing beyond the mask they present to the world. Imagine using this superpower in your relationships. Your experiences can be a bridge to understanding and supporting your loved ones in their battles, whether they're dealing with mental health issues, personal losses, or just the everyday stressors of life.

This enhanced empathy enriches your relationships and can alter your dynamic with others, fostering a deeper mutual understanding and respect. It's a bit like having an emotional X-ray vision; you're able to see beneath the surface, to the heart of what others are feeling, which can be incredibly comforting to those you love.

Building Supportive Networks

Now, about building those supportive networks—they're essential, like having a personal team of cheerleaders, therapists, and strategists all rolled into one. Creating this network involves reaching out to others who share your sensitivity to the human condition, perhaps those you meet in therapy groups, online communities, or even within your existing social circles who demonstrate an understanding of mental health challenges.

But here's the key: these networks need to be reciprocal. They're not just about getting support but about giving it, too. It's a two-way street where care and understanding flow freely in both directions. Think of it as a garden everyone tends to, where the fruits of labor benefit all who contribute. By nurturing this network, you ensure that support is there when you need it, just as you provide a shoulder or an ear when others need it.

Positive Role Modeling

Lastly, embracing your role as a positive relationship model can have a ripple effect. By managing your bipolar disorder openly and responsibly, you demonstrate that while the disorder is a part of your life, it doesn't define your entirety. You show that it's possible to live a full, productive, and loving life, which can be incredibly inspiring to others. Whether showing resilience in the face of challenges or advocating for mental health awareness, you're setting an example that challenges stigma and encourages a broader dialogue about mental health.

In your relationships, this modeling can teach others about resilience, the importance of mental health care, and the power of empathy. It's about showing—not just telling—that it's okay to have struggles and that they don't have to overshadow your achievements or worth. By being this role model, you not only change how others view bipolar disorder but also how they treat those who live with it, fostering a more understanding and supportive community around you.

In weaving these threads of vulnerability, empathy, supportive networks, and positive role modeling into the fabric of your relationships, you transform potential obstacles into opportunities for growth and connection. It's about turning your unique challenges into strengths that support your personal journey and enrich the lives of everyone around you. Through this process, your relationships become more profound, meaningful, and resilient—true testaments to the power of openness, understanding, and mutual support.

9.5 Setting and Achieving Personal Goals with Bipolar

Navigating life with bipolar disorder often feels like you're trying to assemble a puzzle on a windy day. When you think you've got a piece in place, a gust comes along, and you're scrambling to keep everything from flying away. But here's a little secret: setting and achieving goals with bipolar isn't about avoiding the wind—it's learning to build a better puzzle board. Let's talk about real-deal strategies for setting goals that stick, no matter the weather.

First things first, the art of goal-setting when you're dealing with bipolar disorder is like being a tailor; it's all about customization. Generic goals just won't fit right. They can be too tight, leaving no room for those days when you need a little more flexibility, or too loose, failing to provide the structure you crave during chaotic times. Start by acknowledging the unique challenges and strengths that come with your bipolar disorder. Perhaps your incredible bursts of energy during manic phases could be channeled into creative projects or brainstorming sessions. In contrast, the reflective nature of your depressive phases might lend itself well to planning or reflective activities. By aligning your goals with the natural ebb and flow of your energy levels, you create a rhythm that works with your bipolar disorder, not against it.

Now, onto the balancing act. Imagine you're a DJ mixing tracks in a club. Each track represents an area of your life—health, relationships, career, hobbies. Achieving balance isn't about giving each track an equal playtime; it's about creating a harmony that feels right for you. This might mean turning up the health track when you feel an episode coming on or dialing up professional aspirations during times of stability. It's crucial to tune into your needs and adjust your life's mix accordingly. This dynamic approach lets you stay responsive to your mental health while pursuing personal growth and professional success. It also means sometimes letting one track fade into the background momentarily to focus on another, knowing you can always bring it back into the mix when the time is right.

Celebrating progress in managing bipolar disorder is like cheering for every mile in a marathon, not just the finish line. No matter how small, every step forward is a victory worth recognizing. Did you make it through a tough week without canceling a single plan? That's a win. Have you managed to stick to your medication schedule despite a hectic week? Another win. These moments build on each other, forming a chain of successes that, over time, reflect significant progress. Whether treating yourself to a night out or simply acknowledging your progress, the celebration reinforces positive behavior and boosts your morale. It's a way to remind yourself that while the road may be long and winding, you are indeed moving forward, one step at a time.

Adjusting goals is an inevitable part of life with bipolar disorder. Think of your goals as living entities; they grow and change as you do. What worked for you last year might not fit this year, and that's okay. The key is to stay flexible, reassess your goals regularly, and adjust them based on your current circumstances and capabilities. Maybe you set a goal to jog daily, but you're finding it clashes with your energy levels some days. Adjusting this goal to be more flexible, perhaps changing it to 'engage in physical activity' so some days that's yoga, others a walk, keeps you moving without the pressure to hit the pavement running. This flexibility respects the dynamic nature of bipolar disorder and helps prevent the frustration that can come from feeling like you're not meeting your own expectations. In this way, adjusting goals isn't a sign of setback; it's a strategy for sustainable success, ensuring your aspirations evolve in tandem with your personal journey.

When setting and achieving goals with bipolar disorder, remember that it's less about the destination and more about crafting a journey that respects your rhythms, celebrates your progress, and adapts to your growth. It's about building that puzzle board solid and steady, so no matter how windy it gets, you can keep adding pieces, watching the picture of your life come together, bit by bit.

9.6 Embracing Change: The Evolving Nature of Bipolar Management

Change, much like that one relative who never RSVPs but always shows up at family gatherings, is inevitable. Especially when you're navigating life with bipolar disorder, where change is as constant as the ebb and flow of the tides, learning to embrace this change, rather than resisting it, can transform your approach to managing bipolar disorder and enhance your personal growth. Think of change as the landscape shifting on a long road trip—yes, it can be unpredictable and sometimes challenging, but it also brings new scenery and fresh perspectives that enrich the journey.

One of the first steps in becoming friends with change is to accept that your bipolar management will evolve. What works for you now might not work next year or even next month, and that's perfectly okay. It's not a sign of failure but a natural part of living with an inherently dynamic condition. Embracing this fact can remove a lot of pressure and open you up to exploring new strategies as your needs shift. This might mean adjusting your medications as your body responds differently over time or switching up your therapy sessions as you enter different phases of your life. It's all about keeping the dialogue with your healthcare providers open and honest, ensuring that your treatment plan stays as agile and adaptable as the disorder itself.

Staying flexible with your treatment plans and personal goals isn't just practical; it's necessary. Flexibility allows you to respond to changes in your mental health landscape with grace rather than frustration. It's like being a skilled surfer, adjusting your balance and stance as the waves change. This agility in managing your disorder can be incredibly empowering. It helps you to maintain control over your well-being, even when bipolar disorder throws a curveball your way. Similarly, your personal goals might need to be fluid. Life doesn't stop when you're managing bipolar disorder; ambitions change, new opportunities arise, and challenges crop up. Keeping your goals flexible means you can recalibrate them to align with your current capabilities and life context, ensuring they remain relevant and achievable.

Incorporating new learning and experiences into your management strategy is also crucial. Just as a chef seeks out new flavors and techniques to keep their dishes exciting, staying informed about the latest research and advancements in bipolar disorder treatment can introduce new tools and options into your management arsenal. Whether it's a new type of therapy, a newly developed medication, or holistic practices that others with bipolar disorder have found helpful, integrating new knowledge not only keeps you at the forefront of managing your condition but also empowers you to make informed decisions about your health care.

Finally, adopting a growth mindset can radically change how you view the challenges posed by bipolar disorder. Instead of seeing them as roadblocks, view them as opportunities to learn and grow. This mindset encourages resilience and a positive outlook, focusing on progress and possibilities rather than limitations. Every challenge you face and navigate successfully builds your confidence and skills, proving to yourself that you can adapt and thrive, no matter what bipolar disorder throws at you. It's about celebrating each small victory and using it as a stepping stone towards more significant achievements. With a growth mindset, every experience—good or bad—is valuable to your continuous journey toward personal and mental health growth.

As this chapter wraps up, remember that embracing change, staying flexible, continuously incorporating new learning, and maintaining a growth mindset are not just strategies for managing bipolar disorder; they are approaches to life. They prepare you to not only adapt to the winds of change but to harness them, steering your ship towards new horizons filled with possibilities. As we transition into the next chapter, let's carry forward this adaptable, open, and growth-focused mindset, exploring further how these principles can be applied to navigating the broader aspects of life with bipolar disorder.

CONCLUSION

Well, here we are at the end of our shared roller-coaster ride—a journey through the peaks and valleys of living with bipolar disorder. From those early days of grappling with the diagnosis, feeling like you've been handed a puzzle without a picture on the box, to now, hopefully, standing a bit taller, armed with strategies, insights, and a dash of humor to tackle the days ahead.

Together, we've traversed the landscape of bipolar disorder, not just surviving but learning how to thrive. I hope I've managed to sprinkle a bit of hope and resilience throughout these pages, illustrating that with the right tools and a hefty dose of perseverance, managing bipolar disorder is not just a possibility but a palpable reality.

Knowledge truly is power—understanding the nuts and bolts of bipolar disorder, from the latest scientific research to the spectrum of effective treatment options, is crucial. It's your armor in the ongoing battle against this condition's unpredictability. And let's not forget about the superpower of self-advocacy—navigating healthcare, personal relationships, and societal stigma with confidence and clarity.

We've talked a lot about the village it takes to manage bipolar disorder effectively. Remember, no one is an island, especially when dealing with such a complex condition. Healthcare providers, family, friends, and peer support groups are your tribe. Lean on them, learn from them, and let them lift you up when it gets tough.

Lifestyle management—oh, what a difference it makes! From tweaking your diet to incorporating exercise, prioritizing sleep, and mastering the art of stress management, these are not just good habits; they're your daily doses of stability.

Now, let's talk about growth. If you ever doubted that you could flourish amidst the chaos of bipolar disorder, let's put those doubts to rest. This journey can lead to profound personal growth, creativity, and a deep empathy that transforms how you view the world and interact with others. What some see as vulnerabilities, you can wield as strengths.

As we close this chapter (literally and metaphorically), I urge you to proudly wear your advocate hat. Share your story, challenge the stigma, and be the beacon of understanding and support the world desperately needs.

But above all, carry with you a message of hope and empowerment. Yes, the road may be bumpy (and trust me, I know a thing or two about bumpy roads), but with the strategies, knowledge, and support systems we've discussed, you are more than equipped to lead a fulfilling life. Keep learning, stay adaptable, and embrace the evolution of your management strategies and personal growth.

Take a moment to reflect on how far you've come since that initial diagnosis. It's not just about managing a condition; it's about recognizing your journey and resilience and celebrating every victory, big or small.

Keep this book close as a reminder of what you've learned and as a companion for those days when you need extra support or a quick refresh on managing symptoms. Remember, managing bipolar disorder is a continuous journey, and I'm so grateful you allowed me to be a part of yours.

Thank you for your trust, your time, and your tenacity. Here's to more good days than bad, to laughter being part of the prescription, and to you—remarkable, resilient you—thriving in all your unique glory. Cheers to moving forward, one step, one laugh, one triumph at a time.

Ivette

REFERENCES

- Promising new bipolar disorder study reveals structural brain changes over time https://keck.usc.edu/news/promising-new-bipolar-disorder-study-reveals-structural-brain-changes-over-time/

- Causes of Bipolar Disorder https://www.webmd.com/bipolar-disorder/bipolar-disorder-causes

- Bipolar 1 vs. Bipolar 2: Know the Difference - Healthline https://www.healthline.com/health/bipolar-disorder/bipolar-1-vs-bipolar-2

- Environmental Risk Factors for Schizophrenia and Bipolar ... https://www.ncbi.nlm.nih.gov/pmc/articles/PMC8273311/

- Diagnosing Bipolar Disorder - NYU Langone Health https://nyulangone.org/conditions/bipolar-disorder/diagnosis

- 9 Essential Coping Strategies for Bipolar Disorder https://www.healthcentral.com/slideshow/essential-coping-strategies-for-bipolar-disorder

- Balancing Bipolar Medications and Their Side Effects https://www.healthline.com/health/bipolar-disorder/managing-medication-side-effects

- How to Build a Support System For Your Mental Health https://mywellbeing.com/therapy-101/how-to-build-a-support-system

- Holistic Treatment for Mood Disorders - Alternative to Meds https://www.alternativetomeds.com/blog/holistic-treatment-for-mood-disorders/

- Lifestyle interventions for bipolar disorders: A systematic ... https://www.sciencedirect.com/science/article/abs/pii/S0149763423002269

- Evidence-Based Psychotherapies for Bipolar Disorder - FOCUS
https://focus.psychiatryonline.org/doi/10.1176/appi.focus.2019
0004

- Balancing Bipolar Medications and Their Side Effects
https://www.healthline.com/health/bipolar-disorder/managing-medication-side-effects

- Accommodations for Employees with Mental Health Conditions https://www.dol.gov/agencies/odep/program-areas/mental-health/maximizing-productivity-accommodations-for-employees-with-psychiatric-disabilities

- 10 Tips for Facing College with Bipolar Disorder
https://www.bphope.com/blog/10-tips-for-facing-college-with-bipolar-disorder/

- The Reciprocal Relationship between Bipolar Disorder and ...
https://pubmed.ncbi.nlm.nih.gov/27862615/#:~:text=Results%3A%20Empathy%20and%20understanding%20from,of%20a%20major%20mood%20episode.

- Art, creativity, and bipolar disorder
https://www.medicalnewstoday.com/articles/bipolar-disorder-art

- Tips for Explaining Bipolar Disorder to Friends and Family
https://www.healthline.com/health/bipolar-disorder/talking-with-loved-ones

- Supporting someone with bipolar disorder - Mind
https://www.mind.org.uk/information-support/types-of-mental-health-problems/bipolar-disorder/supporting-someone-with-bipolar/

- Parenting with Bipolar Disorder: Coping with Risk of Mood ...
https://www.ncbi.nlm.nih.gov/pmc/articles/PMC3963259/

- Bipolar Disorder and Crumbling Relationships: Coping With a Bipolar Loved One
https://highconflictinstitute.com/mental-health/bipolar-

disorder-and-crumbling-relationships-coping-with-a-bipolar-
loved-one/

● DBSA Support Groups
https://www.dbsalliance.org/helping-a-friend-or-family-
member/dbsa-support-groups/

● Find Support Groups https://www.mhanational.org/find-
support-groups

● Bipolar disorder: Finding the right therapist and more
https://www.medicalnewstoday.com/articles/right-therapist-
for-bipolar-disorder

● How to Practice Self-Care with Bipolar Disorder
https://www.healthline.com/health/bipolar-disorder/self-care

● Strategies to Reduce Mental Illness Stigma
https://www.ncbi.nlm.nih.gov/pmc/articles/PMC8835394/

● Living with bipolar disorder: Employment and more
https://www.medicalnewstoday.com/articles/bipolar-and-
work#:~:text=The%20ADA%20protects%20people%20with,p
rotects%20people%20with%20bipolar%20disorder.

● Bipolar Disorder: Relapse Warning Signs | Article
https://www.therapistaid.com/therapy-guide/bipolar-early-
warning-signs

● Bipolar Help: Living with Bipolar Disorder -
HelpGuide.org https://www.helpguide.org/articles/bipolar-
disorder/living-with-bipolar-disorder.htm

● Setting & Achieving Goals - Depression and Bipolar
Support ... https://www.dbsalliance.org/setting-achieving-
goals/

● Art, creativity, and bipolar disorder
https://www.medicalnewstoday.com/articles/bipolar-disorder-
art

● How Lifelong Learning Benefits Your Mental Health
https://www.transformationsnetwork.com/post/how-lifelong-
learning-benefits-your-mental-health

- Evidence-Based Psychotherapies for Bipolar Disorder - PMC
https://www.ncbi.nlm.nih.gov/pmc/articles/PMC6999214